What to do when you can't add and subtract

By
Steve Chinn

Egon Publishers Ltd
618 Leeds Road, Outwood, Wakefield, WF1 2LT

What to do when you can't add and subtract

First published 1999
Second Edition 2009

Egon Publishers Ltd
618 Leeds Road, Outwood
Wakefield WF1 2LT

Tel/FAX: 01924 871697

www.egon.co.uk
information@egon.co.uk

ISBN: 978 1904160 94 6

There are 5 books in this series :-
What to do when you can't multiply and divide
What to do when you can't learn the times tables
What to do when you can't add and subtract
What to do when you can't do fractions, decimals and percentages
What to do when you can't tell the time

Typeset by Omega Cottage DTP and Web Design
Tingley, Wakefield

Why this book?

Mathematics is a very developmental subject. What and how you learn the basics will have a huge influence on future learning. This book is about early, basic maths skills; about understanding numbers and how they are used.

The methods described in this book have been developed to circumvent the barriers that many learners experience when trying to learn maths.

As the book progresses, different ideas, explanations and methods are described. It is important to realise that not all methods work for everyone. Learners have to experiment and find what works for them.

The work in this book is based on years of classroom experience and research with learners who often struggled to understand maths.

What is addition? What is subtraction?

Basically: **addition is putting together**

Basically: **subtraction is taking apart**

This makes addition and subtraction opposite versions of the same procedure.

Examples: (It may help if you actually set up these demonstrations with coins or counters and move them as shown.)

Addition   6 + 3 = 9

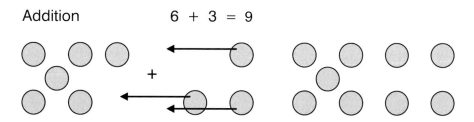

Subtraction   9   –   3

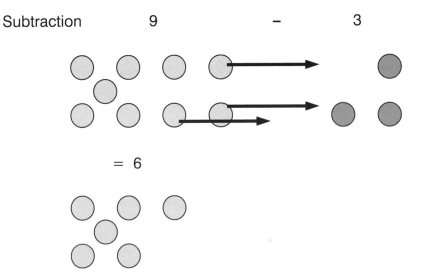

= 6

Adding 6 and 3 gives 9. Taking 3 from 9 takes you back to 6.

Try this 9, 6, 3 example with coins or counters.

Put out 6 counters and 3 counters.

Put them together (add) to give 9.

Then take away (subtract) 3 counters to leave 6.

Extra Stuff # 1. Patterns

In this book when there are diagrams of coins and counters they are set out in the same patterns, for example:

4 is   ⊙ ⊙ / ⊙ ⊙   5 is   ⊙ ⊙ / ⊙ / ⊙ ⊙   8 is   ⊙ ⊙ / ⊙ / ⊙ ⊙   ⊙ ⊙ / ⊙

These consistent patterns are to make the number of coins recognisable. If the coins were arranged randomly we would not be able quickly to know their number, especially once that number gets to 5 and above.

It is one of the ways this book tries to build a sense of number and number values.

Extra Stuff # 2. Numbers in numbers

One of the key ideas used in this book is that a number, any number, is made up from other numbers. For example, one of the ways to 'see' 3 is as 2 + 1.

Splitting a number into parts is called 'partitioning'. For example, two and three digit numbers are often partitioned according to their place values:

> 47 is partitioned as 40 + 7

> 628 is partitioned as 600 + 20 + 8

This book suggests other ways of partitioning as well, where the numbers are the 'easy' numbers, that is 1   2   5   10   20   50, and so on.

This means that 47 is partitioned as   20 + 20 + 5 + 2, and
      628 is partitioned as 500 + 100 + 20 + 5 + 2 + 1.

This action could be compared to setting up money values in coins, for example, 86p could be made from:

$$50p + 20p + 10p + 5p + 1p$$

A second example of the relationship between adding and subtracting:

Addition: $\qquad$ $20 + 4 = 24$

Subtraction: $\qquad$ $24 - 4 = 20$

Adding 20 and 4 gives 24.
Subtracting 4 from 24 takes you back to 20.

A third example:

$$136 + 23 = 159$$

$$159 - 23 = 136$$

Adding 136 and 23 gives 159.
Taking 23 from 159 takes you back to 136.

Extra Stuff # 3. Counting

Counting is a basic skill. It is how we begin to deal with quantities. Counting is, however, only an efficient process with small quantities. In order to become 'good' at maths we have to develop skills beyond counting.

Learners need to progress beyond counting to become efficient at arithmetic and mathematics.

According to the UK neuro-psychology of maths expert Professor Brian Butterworth ("Google" *'Mathematical Brain'*) the two important pre-requisite skills for developing a good ability with maths are:

- the ability to see a random cluster of dots and know how many are there
- the ability to compare with security and accuracy the value of digits (A digit is 0, 1, 2, 3, 4, 5, 6, 7, 8, or 9)

As adults we can see and accurately identify about 5 dots, even if those dots are only presented briefly. We can do this in two ways:

1) We can just recognise and know how many are there, or
2) We can visualise the pattern in our memory and count them.

Obviously, the first method is quicker.

There is some research to suggest that children who are trained in this task improve in their general maths achievements.

I interpret the importance of this skill as showing that we should not always have to count to know the value of a cluster of objects. We need to start to form a concept of numbers and their values.

Digits are the alphabet of arithmetic. It is important to know them, to recognise them, to know what value they represent and to be able to compare their relative values.

BASIC ADDITION AND SUBTRACTION FACTS
(Also called number bonds)

It is possible to use counting to access the answers for these facts, however, a complete dependence on counting is not going to help you develop an understanding of numbers.

In this section methods to help you access these facts and reduce a dependence on counting are explained.

The basic facts are the addition of any combination of two numbers from 0 to 10, for example,

$$4 + 8 = 12 \quad \text{or} \quad 10 + 7 = 17 \quad \text{or} \quad 10 + 9 = 19$$

The basic subtraction facts are the opposite facts

$$12 - 8 = 4 \quad \text{and} \quad 12 - 4 = 8$$

$$17 - 10 = 7 \quad \text{and} \quad 17 - 7 = 10$$

$$19 - 10 = 9 \quad \text{and} \quad 19 - 9 = 10$$

Note that there are two subtraction facts for each addition fact (unless the numbers being added are the same as with $6 + 6 = 12$)

It does not matter in which order the numbers are added, but it does matter in which order they are subtracted.

You can show this with coins, as shown below for 5 and 4 and 9.

Try it!

a) $5 + 4 = 9$ b) $4 + 5 = 9$

c) $9 - 4 = 5$ d) $9 - 5 = 4$

a) 5 + 4 = 9

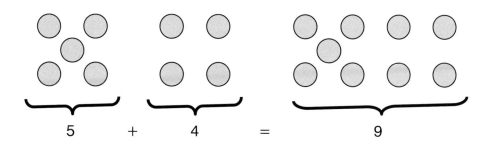

        5   +   4   =   9

b) 4 + 5 = 9

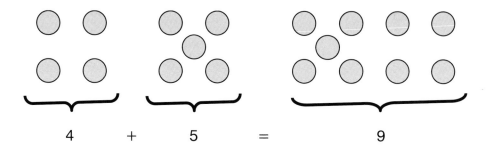

        4   +   5   =   9

c) 9 – 4 = 5

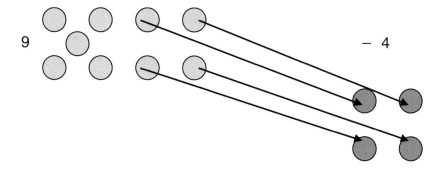

9   – 4

= 5

d) $9 - 5 = 4$

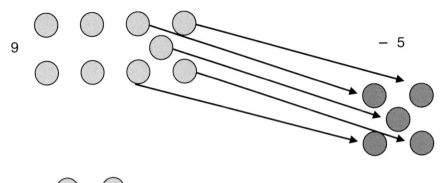

9

− 5

= 4

Extra stuff # 4

The technical term for the fact that the answer is the same whatever order you use to add two numbers is 'commutative'.

Commutative means interchangeable.

For those who understand algebra, we can use this maths tool to express the commutative property.

If we represent the first number as A and the second number as B, then

$$A + B = B + A$$

For example, if A stands for 8 and B stands for 5, then:

$$8 + 5 = 5 + 8 \ (= 13)$$

It will be a great help with addition and subtraction sums if you can memorise or learn to work out quickly the basic addition and subtraction facts. BUT : –

Not everyone can recall these facts from memory, especially if they have to do this quickly.

Strategies to help you to retrieve basic facts

Some useful strategies to help you deal with this problem are described below. Even if you can finger count the facts quickly, the strategies described below will be better because they will help you to understand the patterns in numbers.

So, if you have difficulties in remembering lots of maths facts, make sure that the ones you do learn are useful and extendable and therefore worth as much as possible.

Most of the basic facts can be inter-related, extended or simplified.

Extra Stuff # 5

A good reason to inter-relate facts is that it strengthens links and helps you to retrieve facts. For example,

A young girl with some learning problems in maths is unable to give the answer to the combination 5 + 6, but if you ask her for 5 + 5, which she knows is 10, she can then answer 'What is 5 + 6?'

The commutative idea applies well to addition facts.

Each addition fact can actually be written as two addition facts and two subtraction facts.

For example,

addition facts, where the total is the same (10):

$$6 + 4 = 10 \qquad \text{is also} \qquad 4 + 6 = 10$$

and subtraction facts, where the answers are not the same:

$$10 - 4 = 6 \qquad \text{and} \qquad 10 - 6 = 4$$

Try this with coins

There are 121 basic addition facts. Approximately half are commutative (which means interchangeable, see above) such as

$$4 + 5 = 9 \qquad \text{and} \qquad 5 + 4 = 9$$

This link alone reduces the learning task to around 60 facts.

The learning task

These 121 addition facts are mirrored by 121 subtraction facts, so, for example:

$$4 + 5 = 9 \qquad \text{and} \qquad 5 + 4 = 9$$

are mirrored by

$$9 - 5 = 4 \qquad \text{and} \qquad 9 - 4 = 5$$

The addition facts can be presented in a square. There are extra addition facts squares at the back of the book and also there are two blank squares for you to fill in to mark your progress.

Addition facts square

+	0	1	2	3	4	5	6	7	8	9	10
0	0	1	2	3	4	5	6	7	8	9	10
1	1	2	3	4	5	6	7	8	9	10	11
2	2	3	4	5	6	7	8	9	10	11	12
3	3	4	5	6	7	8	9	10	11	12	13
4	4	5	6	7	8	9	10	11	12	13	14
5	5	6	7	8	9	10	11	12	13	14	15
6	6	7	8	9	10	11	12	13	14	15	16
7	7	8	9	10	11	12	13	14	15	16	17
8	8	9	10	11	12	13	14	15	16	17	18
9	9	10	11	12	13	14	15	16	17	18	19
10	10	11	12	13	14	15	16	17	18	19	20

**Strategies for learning and accessing the
addition and subtraction facts**

The idea behind these strategies is to remember some key facts and
have easy ways of working out the other facts. The strategies are
based on using some key facts:

- **Understanding what to do with zero, 0**
- **Counting on (1, 2, 3) and counting back (3, 2, 1)**
- **Adding on 10. Subtracting 10**
- **Adding on 9. Subtracting 9**
- **Using number bonds for 10**
- **Using doubles (e.g. 3 + 3 or 6 + 6)**

These strategies will also help you to develop an understanding of
numbers and number values.

Zero 0

When you add zero, 0, to any number, the number stays the same and
thus has the same value.

For example: $5 + 0 = 5$ $13 + 0 = 13$

When you subtract zero, 0, from any number, the number stays the
same and thus has the same value.

For example: $5 - 0 = 5$ $13 - 0 = 13$

Extra Stuff # 6. Understanding zero 0 and place value

0 or zero is used to represent the idea of nothing. Nothing doesn't sound like a very useful idea for arithmetic, but it is very important in how we write and understand the value of numbers.

The ancient Romans had no symbol for zero, working on the principle that if zero meant nothing, why would you need a symbol for it!

One of the ways we use zero is key to the concept of place value in number.

Counting from 1 to 9 takes you through all the unit digits:

$$1 \quad 2 \quad 3 \quad 4 \quad 5 \quad 6 \quad 7 \quad 8 \quad 9$$

The next number in this sequence is ten, 10, which has two digits, a 1 and a 0.

Our number system is based on us having ten fingers. We can use each finger for counting until we reach ten. We can then register 10 and count fingers again until we once more reach 10. That is now two tens.

$$10 \quad 11 \quad 12 \quad 13 \quad 14 \quad 15 \quad 16 \quad 17 \quad 18 \quad 19 \quad 20$$

These numbers, which consist of two digits in set positions are the foundation of place value and the base ten system.

For example, in 17, the 1 is one ten and the 7 is seven units.

If the counting continues:

$$21 \quad 22 \quad 23 \quad 24 \quad 25 \quad 26 \quad 27 \quad 28 \quad 29 \quad 30$$

then in 28, the 2 represents 2 tens and the 8 represents 8 units.

One of the easier experiences of the use of zero in place value for most people is its use with the tens, the two digit numbers, known as decades, that is ten (10), twenty (20), thirty (30), forty (40), fifty (50), sixty (60), seventy (70), eighty (80) and ninety (90).

In each of these tens numbers the zero, 0, is used to tell us that there are no units and also to push the tens digit into the place value position for tens.

In 3 the 3 is three units.

In 30 the 3 is thirty, three tens.

In 300 the 3 is three hundreds.

In 3000 the 3 is three thousands.

In these examples, the zero is used to give the 3 its place value: tens, hundreds or thousands.

In a three digit number, such as 321, the 3 represents 300, the 2 is 20 and the 1 is 1.

And, in another example of a three digit number, 704, the zero means there are no tens. The zero pushes the 7 into the hundreds place.

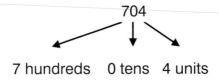

704

7 hundreds   0 tens   4 units

If you did not use the zero, 704 would be 74 (seventy four), so one of zero's important uses is to push other digits into their correct place value.

So the value of a digit in a number depends on its place in that number: place value.

Adding and subtracting zero

Zero acts as nothing when it is added to or subtracted from another number.

Adding nothing to and subtracting nothing from a number does not change the number. For example,

$$5 + 0 = 5 \qquad\qquad 5 - 0 = 5$$
$$10 + 0 = 10 \qquad\qquad 10 - 0 = 10$$

This means that the zero facts are easy to learn.

Progress Report # 1

Once you know the zero addition facts you have mastered 21 facts from the addition square.

100 facts to go!

Adding 1, 2 and 3 (by counting on)
Subtracting 1, 2 and 3 (by counting back)

It is very quick to finger count on or back 1, 2 or 3.

Always add on the small number to the bigger number, for example with 2 + 8, add 2 onto the 8, counting 9, **10**.

It is also quick to finger count back to subtract 1, 2 or 3, for example with 7 – 3, count back from 7, counting, 6, 5, **4**.

Or it is possible to do a subtraction by finger counting from the lower number to the target number, for example 10 – 8 is counted as 2 numbers on from 8, counting 9, **10**.

Practise and aim to be accurate and quick. (Being quick, not rushed, can help your short term memory cope better with the rest of the sum. Being rushed may weaken your short term memory.)

Remember that each addition fact is two facts:
(except for 'doubles': 1 + 1, 2 + 2 etc.)

So,   5 + 1   and   1 + 5   both equal 6

                   5 + 1 = 6   and   1 + 5 = 6

Progress Report #2

Once you can add on 1, 2 and 3, you have mastered another 51 facts on the addition square:

49 facts left to learn.

Note: You could shade in these facts on a blank addition/subtraction square (see back of this book). Use different colours for each set of facts. Some colours will overlap.

Adding on 10. Subtracting 10

Ten has two digits, a 1 and a 0. The zero means there are no units.
This means that adding units to 10 is easy. The added unit goes
straight into the unit place, unchanged. It is adding a number to
nothing. The digit doesn't change, it just gets added to the zero.
Effectively it replaces the zero.

Look at the pattern: It also makes easy subtractions:

$$10 + 1 = 11 \qquad 19 - 9 = 10$$
$$10 + 2 = 12 \qquad 18 - 8 = 10$$
$$10 + 3 = 13 \qquad 17 - 7 = 10$$
$$10 + 4 = 14 \qquad 16 - 6 = 10$$
$$10 + 5 = 15 \qquad 15 - 5 = 10$$
$$10 + 6 = 16 \qquad 14 - 4 = 10$$
$$10 + 7 = 17 \qquad 13 - 3 = 10$$
$$10 + 8 = 18 \qquad 12 - 2 = 10$$
$$10 + 9 = 19 \qquad 11 - 1 = 10$$

Try this with coins. Use 1p and 10p coins. For example, 10 + 6

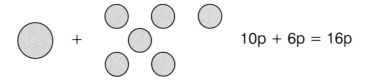

$$10p + 6p = 16p$$

The 10p coin represents 1 ten and 0 units, so adding six 1p coins
makes 1 ten and 6 units, that is 16p.

ADDING 10

10 + 1 = 11	1 + 10 = 11
10 + 2 = 12	2 + 10 = 12
10 + 3 = 13	3 + 10 = 13
10 + 4 = 14	4 + 10 = 14
10 + 5 = 15	5 + 10 = 15
10 + 6 = 16	6 + 10 = 16
10 + 7 = 17	7 + 10 = 17
10 + 8 = 18	8 + 10 = 18
10 + 9 = 19	9 + 10 = 19
10 + 10 = 20	10 + 10 = 20

SUBTRACTING 10

11 − 1 = 10	11 − 10 = 1
12 − 2 = 10	12 − 10 = 2
13 − 3 = 10	13 − 10 = 3
14 − 4 = 10	14 − 10 = 4
15 − 5 = 10	15 − 10 = 5
16 − 6 = 10	16 − 10 = 6
17 − 7 = 10	17 − 10 = 7
18 − 8 = 10	18 − 10 = 8
19 − 9 = 10	19 − 10 = 9
20 − 10 = 10	20 − 10 = 10

Progress Report # 3

The addition facts for 10 give you 13 'new' facts.

36 to go.

Use another colour to shade in the 10 facts on your blank addition/ subtraction square.

Extra Stuff # 7. A powerful learning technique

This is based on some work I did with Dr Colin Lane (ARROW) in 1984. Try recording a few of the addition and subtraction facts on a PC and then playing them back, repeatedly, preferably through headphones, while looking at the written version on screen.

If you say them at the same time as you hear them, then you are using eyes, ears and voice to push each fact into your memory.

SELF VOICE ECHO can be a very powerful learning idea. Like many techniques, it will work very well for some and less well for others. The only way to find out if it will work for you is to give it a try. When it does work, my experience is that what is remembered is retained for a long time.

"Google" 'self-voice' to find out more about Dr Lane and ARROW.

Doubles

**The 'doubles' (for example, 3 + 3 or 7 + 7) are key facts.
It will be a collection of very useful facts if they can be learned.**

Note that the answers to the doubles **addition** facts are all **even numbers**. This is true even if the numbers being added are odd, for example, adding the odd numbers 3 and 3:

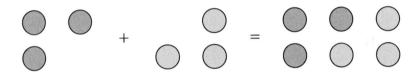

3 is made from 2 and 1. When two threes are added, the ones combine to make 2, an even number. The two twos (2 is an even number) combine to make 4 which is also even.

    Odd number plus odd number   = even number

    Even number plus even number = even number

DOUBLES

$0 + 0 = 0$		$0 - 0 = 0$
$1 + 1 = 2$		$2 - 1 = 1$
$2 + 2 = 4$		$4 - 2 = 2$
$3 + 3 = 6$		$6 - 3 = 3$
$4 + 4 = 8$		$8 - 4 = 4$
$5 + 5 = 10$		$10 - 5 = 5$
$6 + 6 = 12$		$12 - 6 = 6$
$7 + 7 = 14$		$14 - 7 = 7$
$8 + 8 = 16$		$16 - 8 = 8$
$9 + 9 = 18$		$18 - 9 = 9$
$10 + 10 = 20$		$20 - 10 = 10$

See page 29 for more on doubles.

Progress Report # 4

This gives 6 new facts,

30 to go.

The remaining 30 facts reduce by half to 15 because of the commutative property.

The commutative property, $A + B = B + A$, is not relevant with the doubles since the two numbers being added are the same. The 'doubles' only give you one fact each, but they are still very good value.This will be explained later.

Shade in these facts on your addition/subtraction square to show your progress.

Extra Stuff # 8

Remember, learning is a very personal and individual activity. An image or material that works for one person may not work for another. This is one of the reasons why this book offers a range of alternatives.

The only way to find out if something works for you is to give it a (fair) trial.

A material or image may just clarify one point in learning. That is fine. Learners may need more than one material or image to help them learn the range of maths facts.

Two hands: ten fingers

When counting on our fingers, the thumb is counted (!) as a finger. We have ten digits. Fingers make ever-available tallies.

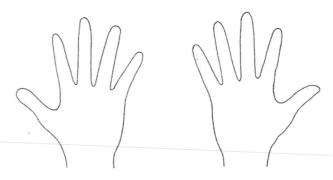

One of the most useful key facts is shown by our hands and fingers

$$5 + 5 = 10$$

We have 10 fingers. This is why our number system uses 10 as its base. This results in key number values such as:

Ten	10	is	10 x 1	(10 lots of one)
Hundred	100	is	10 x 10	(10 lots of ten)
Thousand	1000	is	10 x 100	(10 lots of hundred)

Extra Stuff # 9

The number 12 used to play a much more important role in our lives. Our money system used to use twelve.

- 12 has its own name: a dozen
- 12 x 12 (144) has its own name: a gross.
- Clocks still use 12

The reason for twelve's popularity goes back to ancient times. People used to count on their fingers by using their thumb to do the counting/ touching. The thumb counted the sections on the 4 fingers and, since each finger has 3 sections, 12 was the total count.

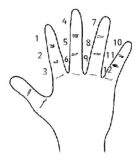

Fingers as tallies

You can also use your 10 fingers as tallies for counting up in twos:

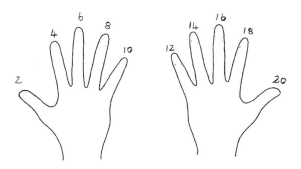

If you have to count in twos beyond 5 x 2 you could shorten the process by starting at the key value, 10, which is 5 x 2.

For example, to count 7 twos, use 7 as 5 + 2:

Start at 5 twos: 10. Count on 2 more twos: 12, 14.

The same use of fingers as tallies can be applied to counting in fives and tens.

Bead Strings

Beads are good for counting and for showing patterns. They make good tallies and add in a kinaesthetic experience to the visual.

The colours help you to move from counting in ones to counting in fives or tens.

Number Lines

Number lines are almost like a bead string, but with symbols. They can be used to show additions and subtractions.

The bigger gradation lines help you group in fives and tens, again moving you on from counting in ones.

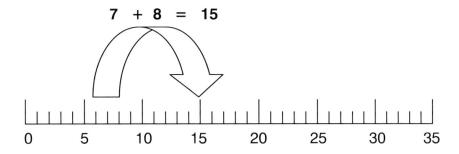

The number line showing 7 + 8 = 15

A ruler can be used as a ready made number line.

Coins

Coins make a good learning aid. They are familiar and offer visual and kinaesthetic experiences.

Another important characteristic of coins (and notes) is that they are only available in the 'easy' values of 1, 2, 5, 10, 20, 50, 100 and so on.

This means they can be used, for example, to count in ones, twos, fives, tens and so on.

Coins are not proportional in size to the values they represent. A 5p coin is not five times as big as a 1p coin, for example. This adds a degree of symbolism, taking the image a little way towards the abstract symbols we use for numbers.

In this book, 1p and 10p coins are used for demonstrating the basic addition and subtraction facts. 5p, 20p or 50p coins are rarely used for these demonstrations.

An example of using coins:

Note the arrangement of the coins to show how numbers break down into the 'easy' key numbers 1,   2   and   5.

For example, the 5 + 1   to   5 + 5 facts break down as shown below:

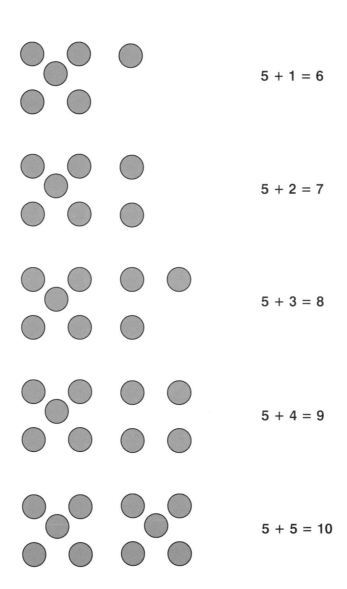

5 + 1 = 6

5 + 2 = 7

5 + 3 = 8

5 + 4 = 9

5 + 5 = 10

27

Stern materials (also used in Numicon)

The materials illustrated which are part of Stern and Numicon are especially effective for illustrating even and odd numbers and the outcomes of adding and subtracting combinations of odd and even numbers.

The shapes clearly show which is an odd number and which is even. Combining two odd numbers creates an even shape (a rectangle).

odd   even   odd   even   odd   even   odd   even   odd   even

Extending the doubles

The doubles are useful facts to learn because they can be used to
access (that is, work out) other facts.

Doubles plus 1

For example: 5 + 5, shown here in coins:

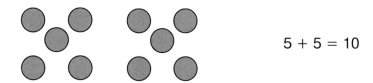

5 + 5 = 10

Adding in 1 more coin will take the answer to 11 (10 + 1 =11). The
extra coin may be added to the first 5 or the second 5 to give two
more facts.

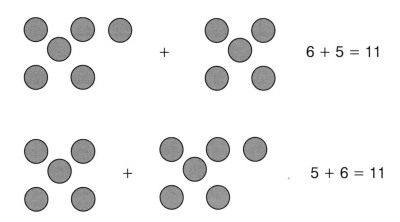

6 + 5 = 11

5 + 6 = 11

This can be done with all the doubles, for example:

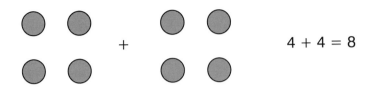

$4 + 4 = 8$

Add 1 to take the answer to 9 (8 + 1 = 9), giving two more addition facts.

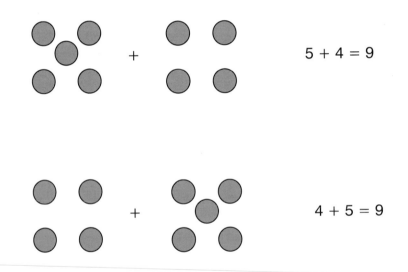

$5 + 4 = 9$

$4 + 5 = 9$

Note that the answers to the addition facts for doubles plus 1 are all **odd numbers.**

Doubles plus 1: The facts

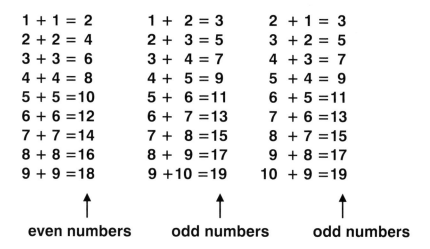

$1 + 1 = 2$	$1 + 2 = 3$	$2 + 1 = 3$
$2 + 2 = 4$	$2 + 3 = 5$	$3 + 2 = 5$
$3 + 3 = 6$	$3 + 4 = 7$	$4 + 3 = 7$
$4 + 4 = 8$	$4 + 5 = 9$	$5 + 4 = 9$
$5 + 5 = 10$	$5 + 6 = 11$	$6 + 5 = 11$
$6 + 6 = 12$	$6 + 7 = 13$	$7 + 6 = 13$
$7 + 7 = 14$	$7 + 8 = 15$	$8 + 7 = 15$
$8 + 8 = 16$	$8 + 9 = 17$	$9 + 8 = 17$
$9 + 9 = 18$	$9 + 10 = 19$	$10 + 9 = 19$
↑	↑	↑
even numbers	**odd numbers**	**odd numbers**

Look at the patterns down each column of answers. The answers to the doubles are a sequence of even numbers. The answers to the doubles plus one are a sequence of odd numbers. Using the coins or the Stern/Numicon materials to work out these facts gives the reason for this. *(An even number plus even number gives an even number. An odd number plus even number gives an odd number.)*

Shade in these facts on a new addition square and look at the pattern. Shade in the doubles facts (in a different colour). Look at the pattern.

Doubles minus 1

A similar argument applies, for example:

$5 + 5 = 10$ becomes $4 + 5 = 9$ and $5 + 4 = 9$

Progress Report #5

You can shade in 10 more addition facts, leaving

20 to learn.

The equivalent subtraction facts for 'doubles plus 1' are:

$3 - 1 = 2$ $3 - 2 = 1$

$5 - 2 = 3$ $5 - 3 = 2$

$7 - 3 = 4$ $7 - 4 = 3$

$9 - 4 = 5$ $9 - 5 = 4$

$11 - 5 = 6$ $11 - 6 = 5$

$13 - 6 = 7$ $13 - 7 = 6$

$15 - 7 = 8$ $15 - 8 = 7$

$17 - 8 = 9$ $17 - 9 = 8$

$19 - 9 = 10$ $19 - 10 = 9$

Look at the pattern of the answers down each column. There is a simple number sequence in each column.

It may help to remember that each starting number in these subtractions is a double plus 1. It often helps to remember how numbers can be broken down (or 'partitioned') . In these examples each starting number breaks down into (or can be partitioned into) a double plus 1. For example, 9 breaks down into $4 + 4 + 1$ and 17 breaks down into $8 + 8 + 1$.

Try setting out some of these examples in coins. For example:

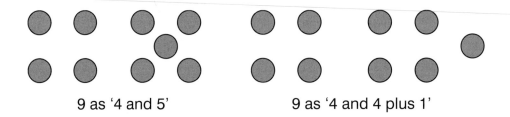

          9 as '4 and 5'   9 as '4 and 4 plus 1'

One of the important skills in maths is to be able to break numbers down (partition them) into easier (or key) numbers or relate them to easier/key numbers *(the 'easier/key' numbers are 1, 2, 5, 10)*.

For example:

9 is 10 − 1

9 is 5 + 4 and 4 + 5

6 is 5 + 1 and 1 + 5

Sharing doubles

I like this strategy. It illustrates another useful concept in arithmetic, that is, you can take a number and divide it into different pairs of numbers whilst keeping the total the same. We shall use this concept when we meet the number bonds for 10.

For example: 4 + 4 = 8   is made into   3 + 5 = 8

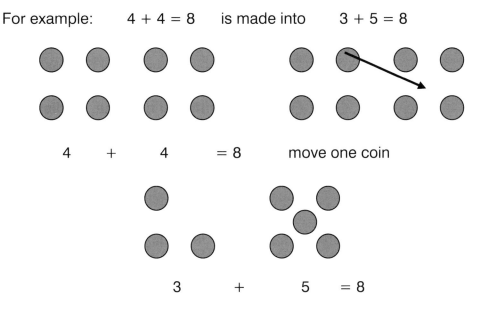

4   +   4   = 8   move one coin

3   +   5   = 8

The total number of coins (8) does not change. The coins are just redistributed or re-partitioned.

A coin can also be moved to make 4 + 4 = 8   become   5 + 3 = 8

Each double fact can become two 'shared double' facts.
Try the list below with coins.

Shared Doubles

2 + 2 = 4	1 + 3 = 4	3 + 1 = 4
3 + 3 = 6	2 + 4 = 6	4 + 2 = 6
4 + 4 = 8	3 + 5 = 8	5 + 3 = 8
5 + 5 = 10	4 + 6 = 10	6 + 4 = 10
6 + 6 = 12	5 + 7 = 12	7 + 5 = 12
7 + 7 = 14	6 + 8 = 14	8 + 6 = 14
8 + 8 = 16	7 + 9 = 16	9 + 7 = 16
9 + 9 = 18	8 + 10 = 18	10 + 8 = 18

Note that each of the 'shared' numbers are either one more or one
less than the double number, so for **6** the shared numbers are 7 (1
more than 6) and 5 (1 less than 6).

Shade in these facts on your (doubles) number square.

Look at each pattern for the doubles, doubles plus 1 and shared
doubles.

Progress Report # 6

The shared doubles have given you 8 new facts.

12 facts left to learn.

Adding on 9

9 is a good example to illustrate why finger counting is slow and inefficient.

A theme in this book is to work with the 'easy/key' numbers, 1, 2, 5 and 10. The easy numbers can be used to help you work with harder numbers. The hard numbers are linked to the easy/key numbers.

9 can be a difficult number, especially if you rely on counting – it takes a lot of counting. But if you use 10 to help, 9 becomes much easier.

The link between 9, the 'hard' number and 10, the 'easy' number is:

9 is 1 less than 10

So, an alternative way to add 9 is to add 10 and take off 1.

Look at some examples: $9 + 8$

Treat the 9 as though it was 10

$$10 + 8 = 18$$

Then take off 1 from 18 to give the answer to $9 + 8$

$$9 + 8 = 17$$

In this strategy, two quick (and easier) steps take the place of one long (harder) step.

Another example: $9 + 6$ is done as $10 + 6 - 1$

$10 + 6 = 16$, then to get $9 + 6$ you subtract the 1: $16 - 1 = 15$

$$9 + 6 = 15$$

Extra Stuff # 10

Try this game with a friend.

Person B has 21 one pence coins and 4 ten pence coins. Person A asks person B to give him 9p. Often person B counts out 9 one pence coins. Person A asks for another 9p and person B again counts out 9 one pence coins. Person A asks for a third 9p, but B only has 3 one pence coins left. B can solve this problem by giving A one 10p coin and taking 1p coin back from A.

This is, of course, an example of $10 - 1 = 9$.

Adding 9

In each case the answer for adding 10 has been printed in **bold** next to the answer for adding 9.

$0 + 9 = 9$ **10**	$9 + 0 = 9$ **10**
$1 + 9 = 10$ **11**	$9 + 1 = 10$ **11**
$2 + 9 = 11$ **12**	$9 + 2 = 11$ **12**
$3 + 9 = 12$ **13**	$9 + 3 = 12$ **13**
$4 + 9 = 13$ **14**	$9 + 4 = 13$ **14**
$5 + 9 = 14$ **15**	$9 + 5 = 14$ **15**
$6 + 9 = 15$ **16**	$9 + 6 = 15$ **16**
$7 + 9 = 16$ **17**	$9 + 7 = 16$ **17**
$8 + 9 = 17$ **18**	$9 + 8 = 17$ **18**
$9 + 9 = 18$ **19**	$9 + 9 = 18$ **19**
$10 + 9 = 19$ **20**	$9 + 10 = 19$ **20**

Other uses of this strategy

This strategy of adding 10 and taking away 1 is useful for adding 9 to any number.

For example:

56 + 9 is done as 56 + 10 = 66, then take off 1 to give the answer 65.

$$56 + 9 = 65$$

It is also useful in those shops which use prices such as £7.99, which is £8.00 minus 1p.

Adding £3.99 + £5.99 + £2.99 can be changed into adding £4 + £6 + £3 by adding 1p to each value.

The 'new' values can be added: 4 + 6 + 3 = 13

And then we subtract 3p, which takes us back to the original values.

That is £13 minus 3p, an answer of £12.97. (see also page 125)

This strategy can also be used for working out 9 times table facts. (See 'What to do when you can't learn the times tables'.)

Extra Stuff # 11

The process of adjusting values such as £3.99 to £4.00 is an example of 'rounding', in this example, rounding to the nearest pound.
When we used 10 − 1 as a way of dealing with 9, we rounded 9 to the nearest 10.

If we see a car priced at £6995, then its price can be rounded to the nearest thousand: £7000.

Rounding can be useful when working out estimates of calculations. We can round up, as in using £10 for £9.95. We can round down as in using £100 for £104.99.

Progress Report # 7

When you can do these addition facts for 9, you have learned 6 more new facts.

Only 6 facts to go.

The remaining facts are:

> **7 + 4 and 4 + 7 (which could be related to 6 + 4)**

> **8 + 4 and 4 + 8 (which could be done as 8 + 2 + 2)**

> **8 + 5 and 5 + 8 (which could be done as 5 + 5 + 3)**

Thanks to the commutative property, there are only 3 independent facts to learn (or count).

Number bonds for 10

These are included as a separate group because of their importance.

These are the pairs of numbers which add together to make 10, for example:

$$3 + 7 = 10 \quad \text{and} \quad 7 + 3 = 10$$

The number bonds for 10 are a family of important and very useful facts.

The Addition/Subtraction Square of basic facts shows the pattern for these number bonds for 10.

10 makes a diagonal line across the square.

+	0	1	2	3	4	5	6	7	8	9	10
0	0	1	2	3	4	5	6	7	8	9	10
1	1	2	3	4	5	6	7	8	9	10	11
2	2	3	4	5	6	7	8	9	10	11	12
3	3	4	5	6	7	8	9	10	11	12	13
4	4	5	6	7	8	9	10	11	12	13	14
5	5	6	7	8	9	10	11	12	13	14	15
6	6	7	8	9	10	11	12	13	14	15	16
7	7	8	9	10	11	12	13	14	15	16	17
8	8	9	10	11	12	13	14	15	16	17	18
9	9	10	11	12	13	14	15	16	17	18	19
10	10	11	12	13	14	15	16	17	18	19	20

$$0 + 10 = 10$$
$$1 + 9 = 10$$
$$2 + 8 = 10$$
$$3 + 7 = 10$$
$$4 + 6 = 10$$

$5 + 5 = 10$ ....This is a key reference fact, related to having 5 fingers on each of our hands

$$6 + 4 = 10$$
$$7 + 3 = 10$$
$$8 + 2 = 10$$
$$9 + 1 = 10$$
$$10 + 0 = 10$$

There are some ways to help remember the number bonds for 10:

1. Look at all your fingers, a total of 10, (for maths purposes your thumbs are counted as fingers!)

A key reference is the obvious, $5 + 5 = 10$. There are 5 fingers on one hand and 5 fingers on the other hand.

The 10 fingers could also be viewed (or grouped) as 1 finger and 9 fingers (1+9), then 2 fingers and 8 fingers (2+8), then 3 fingers and 7 fingers (3+7), then 4 fingers and 6 fingers (4+6), then 5 fingers and 5 fingers (5+5), then 6 fingers and 4 fingers (6+4).
Which then starts the move to the commutative facts: 7 fingers and 3 fingers (7+3), then 8 fingers and 2 fingers (8+2), then 9 fingers and 1 finger (9+1).

40

This is another good example of the connection between addition and subtraction facts. We started by looking at how 10 (fingers) could separate into two numbers.

For example, if we have 2 fingers separated from 10 fingers, this leaves 8 fingers: 10 – 2 = 8.

We then used this partition of 10 as an addition fact 8 + 2 = 10.

2. Use a stack of 10 Lego (or any) bricks. The stack of 10 can be separated as:

9 + 1
8 + 2
7 + 3
6 + 4
5 + 5
4 + 6
3 + 7
2 + 8
1 + 9

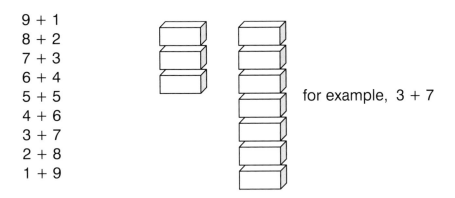

for example, 3 + 7

3. This representation of the facts using symbols/digits sometimes helps:

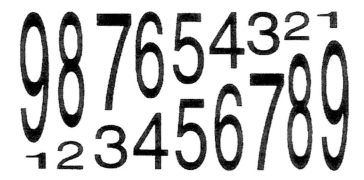

4. Cuisenaire rods. These do not have markings to enable you to count their lengths. (Though connecting rods are now available.) You have to 'know' the value/length of a rod by comparison to other rods and by colour This means that the rods are good for developing links between number values without using counting, and for multisendory learning.

5. Bead Strings

Bead strings are tactile and kinaesthetic. The ten-bead string has a characteristic that is helpful for understanding the number bonds for 10. It holds the ten beads: no beads can be added or taken away. The 10 is conserved, which means that however the beads are split the total must always be 10. Conservation is a fundamental early concept in maths.

Number bonds for 10 (again)

$0 + 10 = 10$			$10 + 0 = 10$	
$1 + 9 = 10$			$9 + 1 = 10$	
$2 + 8 = 10$			$8 + 2 = 10$	
$3 + 7 = 10$			$7 + 3 = 10$	
$4 + 6 = 10$			$6 + 4 = 10$	
$5 + 5 = 10$			$5 + 5 = 10$	
$6 + 4 = 10$			$4 + 6 = 10$	
$7 + 3 = 10$			$3 + 7 = 10$	
$8 + 2 = 10$			$2 + 8 = 10$	
$9 + 1 = 10$			$1 + 9 = 10$	
$10 + 0 = 10$			$0 + 10 = 10$	

The equivalent subtraction facts are;

$$10 - 0 = 10$$
$$10 - 1 = 9$$
$$10 - 2 = 8$$
$$10 - 3 = 7$$
$$10 - 4 = 6$$
$$10 - 5 = 5$$
$$10 - 6 = 4$$
$$10 - 7 = 3$$
$$10 - 8 = 2$$
$$10 - 9 = 1$$
$$10 - 10 = 0$$

Building more facts using the number bonds for 10

Number bonds for 11: Adding 1 to the number bonds for 10.

We extended the doubles facts by adding 1. We can do this with the number bonds for 10. This gives us number bonds for 10 + 1 that is the number bonds for 11.

For example:

$$5 + 5 = 10 \qquad \text{so} \qquad 6 + 5 = 11 \qquad \text{and} \qquad 5 + 6 = 11$$

A visual image for this can be created with coins. Set up 10 coins like this:

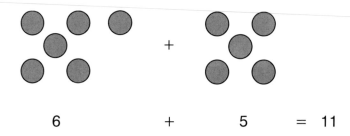

| 5 | + | 5 | = 10 |

Add one coin making

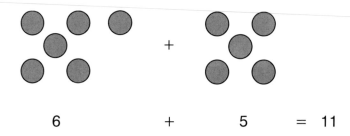

| 6 | + | 5 | = 11 |

or add the coin to the other five coins:

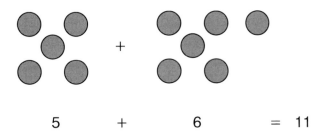

$$5 \quad + \quad 6 \quad = \quad 11$$

Number bonds for 9: Subtracting 1 from the number bonds for 10:

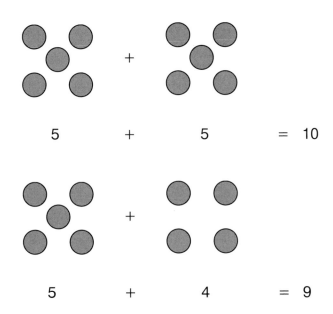

$$5 \quad + \quad 5 \quad = \quad 10$$

$$5 \quad + \quad 4 \quad = \quad 9$$

Number bonds for 100. #1

If the 1p coins are replaced by 10p coins, then the number bonds to 100 are demonstrated. For example:

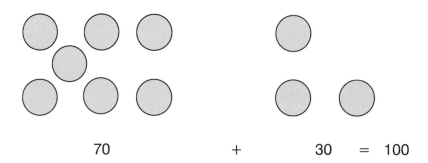

70   +   30   =   100

This pattern is a development of the pattern for the number bonds for 10.

$$
\begin{aligned}
0 &+ 100 = 100 \\
10 &+ \ 90 = 100 \\
20 &+ \ 80 = 100 \\
30 &+ \ 70 = 100 \\
40 &+ \ 60 = 100 \\
50 &+ \ 50 = 100 \\
60 &+ \ 40 = 100 \\
70 &+ \ 30 = 100 \\
80 &+ \ 20 = 100 \\
90 &+ \ 10 = 100 \\
100 &+ \ \ 0 = 100
\end{aligned}
$$

Number bonds for 100. #2

We can combine the patterns for 100 and 10 to develop a further set of bonds for 100.

Start with 10p coins as above:

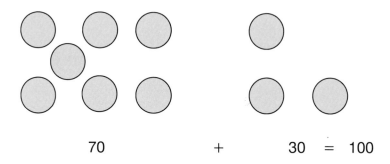

70   +   30   =   100

A mix of 10p coins and ten 1p coins give two stage pattern.
For example: 76 + 24

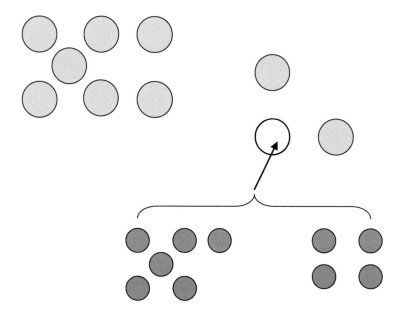

Start with the 1p (units) coins:

$$6 + 4 = 10$$

Then add the 10p coins,
including the 10p made from the ten 1p coins:

$$70 + 20 + 10 = 100$$

The number bonds for 10 and the extension for 100 are used in this example.

Practice:

Check if these make 100:

32 + 68	47 + 43	81 + 19
53 + 46	73 + 27	63 + 37
26 + 84	49 + 51	95 + 15

Number bonds for 1.0

The same number bonds apply to decimal numbers, for example, the decimal number bonds for 1.0.

$$0 \ + \ 1.0 = 1.0$$
$$0.1 + 0.9 = 1.0$$
$$0.2 + 0.8 = 1.0$$
$$0.3 + 0.7 = 1.0$$
$$0.4 + 0.6 = 1.0$$

0.5 + 0.5 = 1.0 ....This is a key reference fact, related to having 5 fingers on each of our hands.

$$0.6 + 0.4 = 1.0$$
$$0.7 + 0.3 = 1.0$$
$$0.8 + 0.2 = 1.0$$
$$0.9 + 0.1 = 1.0$$
$$1.0 + 0.0 = 1.0$$

For more work with taking out 10s, see p119.

Final reminder note on basic addition and subtraction facts

It does not matter which number you ADD to which, the answer is the same.

For example: $6 + 7 = 13$ $7 + 6 = 13$

It DOES matter which number you SUBTRACT from which, the answer will NOT be the same.

For example: $9 - 3 = 6$ $3 - 9 = -6$ (minus 6)

49

Study skills

Now that you have seen how the addition and subtraction facts relate and build together you have to use the information to help your memory and to help you understand numbers and arithmetic.

The basic advice is **PRACTISE,** but practise the facts that have the most use!

Any skill whether it is soccer, playing the violin or doing mathematics needs regular practice. **Little and often** usually works best.

It may sound obvious, but **make sure that what you practise is correct**! You need to make sure that what goes into your brain is correct information, not information that will confuse.

Vary the practice to give different input and help maintain interest. For example, sometimes write down work (or use a computer), sometimes talk it through to yourself or with someone else. Use money to help picture what is happening and make the processes clearer, (understanding helps memory).

Materials also make learning multi-sensory, which means that you are putting the information into your brain using several senses, vision, hearing, speech, touch and movement. These inputs should help fix the information in the brain.

Look around and see where maths comes into your life. Look for number patterns.

**Don't be passive! Work out your change in shops, etc.
Use estimates to check bills. Estimate journey times.
Learn to be confident with numbers!
Everyone makes mistakes.
Don't let mistakes stop you learning.**

Trading

Before we take a careful look at addition and subtraction problems, you have to learn about a process used in both: trading.

Trading is the process of exchanging things of equal value:

10 units into 1 ten:
For example, 10 one pence coins for 1 ten pence coin:

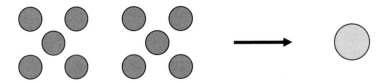

and, the reverse trade:

1 ten into 10 units:
For example, 1 ten pence coin for 10 one pence coins:

10 tens into 1 hundred:
For example, 10 ten pence coins for 1 pound coin (100 pence):

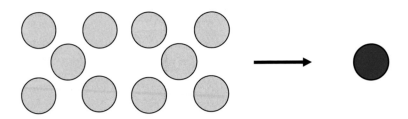

1 hundred into 10 tens:
For example, 1 pound coin (100 pence) for 10 ten pence coins:

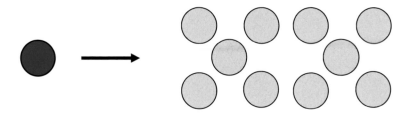

Trading is also about moving between place values, units to tens, tens to units, tens to hundreds and hundreds to tens.

Trading is used in addition and subtraction sums. But, not in every sum. See if you can spot a pattern in the cases where trading is used.

Adding without trading

For example, 4 + 3 = 7

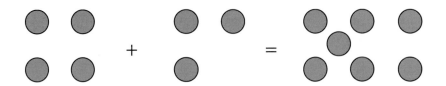

For example, 20 + 20 = 40

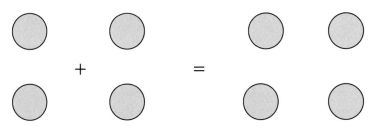

Adding with trading

For example, 7 + 6 = 13

The answer is thirteen, 13. Thirteen, 13, is one ten and three units.

If we use coins to show what happens:

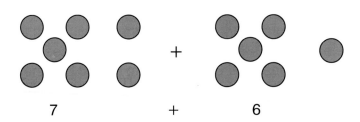

We can trade 10 one pence coins for 1 ten pence coin:

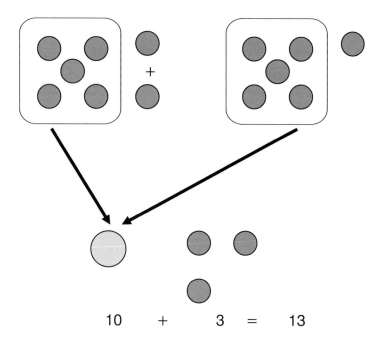

10   +   3   =   13

Now consider the subtraction, 13 minus 6

$$13 - 6 = 7$$

If we start where we ended the addition sum (7 + 6 = 13), that is with 13 as one ten and three units:

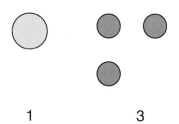

1   3

We do not have enough one pence coins to take six away. To obtain some more one pence coins we trade 1 ten pence coin for 10 one pence coins. This gives us thirteen one pence coins.

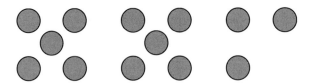

Now take away (subtract) 6, leaving 7.

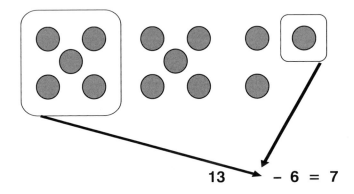

$$13 - 6 = 7$$

The addition and the subtraction both use trading.

In addition the trade is to take 10 x 1p and trade for 1 x 10p.

In subtraction the trade is to take 1 x 10p and trade for 10 x 1p.

This means that we can write numbers in a way that shows trading has been used.

Usually we write this for subtraction:

For example, with the subtraction **72 – 48** the units subtraction has to take 8 from 2.

Trading 1 ten from the 72 for 10 units changes 72 from:

7 tens and 2 units   to   6 tens and 12 units.

This gives us two versions of 72.
Both, of course, add together to make 72.

$$72 \quad = \quad 70 + 2$$
$$72 \quad = \quad 60 + 12$$

We can show this with coins:

72 as 70 + 2: 7 tens plus 2 units

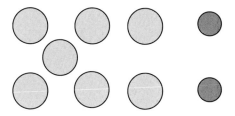

We use trading to 'rename' 72.

72 as 60 + 12: 6 tens and 12 units

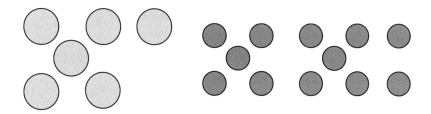

This also works with tens.
For example, we use trading to 'rename' 432:

432 as 400 + 30 + 2: 4 hundreds and 3 tens and 2 units:

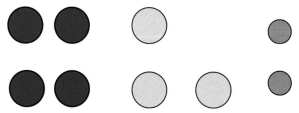

We could also 'rename' 432, with trading, as:

432 as 300 + 130 + 2: 3 hundreds and 13 tens and 2 units:

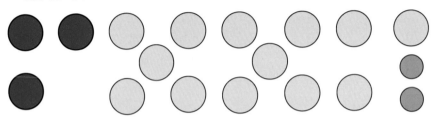

Practice:

Follow the example above to rename and create more units.

Example: 96 = 80 + 16

a) 52   b) 75   c) 39   d) 63

e) 84   f) 93   g) 47

Follow the example above to rename and create more tens.

Example: 751 = 600 + 150 + 1

a) 324   b) 765   c) 283   d) 731

e) 647   f) 815   g) 924

ADDING AND SUBTRACTING. Written methods

This section will explain how to add and subtract when you have paper and a pen available. If you now know your basic facts, that will help. If you do not, you will be a little slower and you should take just a little more care. The practice will be beneficial.

Extra Stuff # 12

Even though you know the basic facts you need to be careful when using them in 'longer' addition and subtraction problems. When using them in these 'dual tasking' situations people sometimes tend to make mistakes (such as 7 + 8 = 14), even though in 'single tasking' they would not make errors.

Main Points

1. Adding and subtracting work to the same procedure – one is a forward process and one is a reverse process.

2. Both procedures use 'trading' (see page 52).

3. Coins can be used to show and demonstrate what is happening. They should follow exactly the same steps as the written method (base ten blocks are also good for demonstrating procedures).

4. You need to remember and understand what place values mean (units, tens, hundreds, etc.).

We will start with a basic example and then build in trading skills to use in 'harder' examples. In each case, the example will be presented in three ways;

1. Money or base ten blocks
2. Place value columns
3. Numbers on their own

Use the presentation which supports your understanding. You will probably start with the money and move to the numbers as your skill improves. Take time to understand what you are doing.

In order to show that addition and subtraction are the same process in opposite directions, each example first adds two numbers and then subtracts to arrive back at the start. Please work through the examples, they are set out to help you to understand the two processes.

Extra Stuff # 13

The word 'trading' is used in this book to label the action of changing ten units into one ten, or one hundred into ten tens. In many traditional settings for learning maths, trading up is often referred to as 'carrying' and trading down is referred to as 'decomposition' or 'renaming'. I prefer 'trading' as it better explains the process and it works whether you are carrying or decomposing.

Adding with no trading

Example: 26 + 43

1. Using coins.

Add together the one pence coins. Add three one pence coins to six one pence coins to make nine one pence coins. The total for the one pence / units column is **9.**

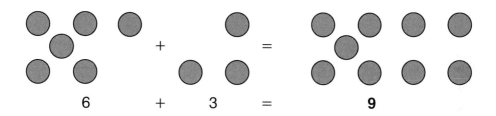

6   +   3   =   9

Now add together the ten pence coins. Add two ten pence coins to four ten pence coins to make six ten pence coins. The total for the ten pence / tens column is **6.**

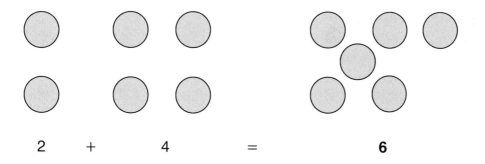

2   +   4   =   6

The answer is 69.

2. Using Base Ten blocks.

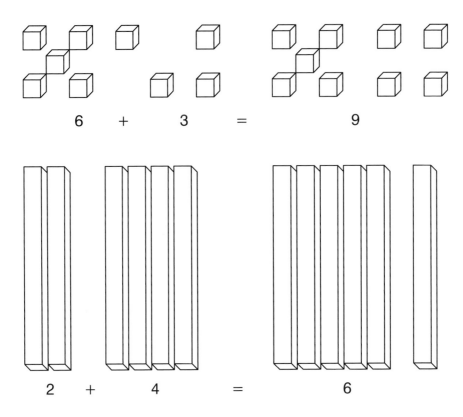

6   +   3   =   9

2   +   4   =   6

The answer is 69.

3. Using place value columns.

Add together the numbers in the units (U) column: $6 + 3 = 9$

Write **9** in the units column on the answer line.

T	U
2	6
+ 4	3
	9

Add together the numbers in the tens (T) column: $2 + 4 = 6$

Write **6** in the tens column on the answer line.

```
T | U
2 | 6
+ 4 | 3
6 | 9
```

The answer is 69.

4. Using numbers on their own.

Add together the units numbers. $6 + 3 = 9$.

Write **9** in the units place of the answer line.

```
  26
+ 43
   9
```

Add together the tens numbers. $2 + 4 = 6$.

Write **6** in the tens place of the answer line.

```
  26
+ 43
  69
```

The answer is 69.

Review
In this addition procedure you start in the units column. You add the two (unit) numbers. The number which is the total from this addition is written in the units column on the answer line. You then add together the numbers in the tens column and write this number in the tens column on the answer line.

Subtracting with no trading (renaming or decomposing)

Example: 69 – 26
(This is the reverse of the addition example from above)

1. Using coins.

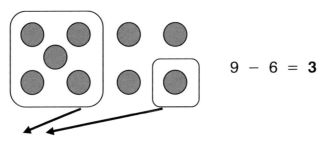

$$9 - 6 = 3$$

Take away 6 one pence coins (units), leaving 3 one pence coins. The answer in the one pence / units column is **3** coins.

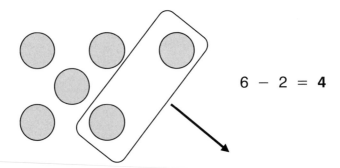

$$6 - 2 = 4$$

Now take away 2 ten pence coins (tens), leaving 4 ten pence coins. The answer in the ten pence / tens column is **4** coins.

The answer is 43.

$$69 - 26 = 43$$

2. Using place value columns.

The top number is 69.
The number you are taking away from this is 26.
Start in the units (U) column: $9 - 6 = 3$.
Write **3** in the units column on the answer line.

$$
\begin{array}{r|r}
\mathbf{T} & \mathbf{U} \\
\hline
6 & 9 \\
-\ 2 & 6 \\
\hline
 & 3 \\
\end{array}
$$

Move to the tens (T) column and subtract from the top number:
     $6 - 2 = 4$
Write **4** in the tens column on the answer line.

$$
\begin{array}{r|r}
\mathbf{T} & \mathbf{U} \\
\hline
6 & 9 \\
-\ 2 & 6 \\
\hline
4 & 3 \\
\end{array}
$$

The answer is 43.

Review

In this subtraction you start in the **units** column. You take away the number in the lower line from the number on the top line and write the answer underneath in the **units** column.

You then take away the **tens** numbers. You take away the number in the lower line from the number on the top line and write the answer underneath in the **tens** column.

Practice exercise:

1a)   45 + 31   1b)   76   –   45

2a)   22 + 75   2b)   97   –   22

(Check your answers to questions 1a, 1b, 2a and 2b (page 36) before you try any more. If you are wrong, read the section again and work through the examples again, using coins to help understanding.)

3a)   54 + 34   3b)   88   –   34

4a)   41 + 23   4b)   64   –   23

For examples of 5 to 10, you should look carefully at both numbers and estimate an answer as a back-up to the accurate procedure.

5)   51 + 32   6)   77   –   47

7)   12 + 53   8)   65   –   34

9)   86 – 55   10)   4   +   42

answers on page 149

Adding with trading across the units / tens columns

In these examples, when the two numbers in the units column are added they will total 10 or more. This will result in trading units for tens (see page 52).

Example: 36 + 57

1. Using coins

Add together the one pence coins. Add 6 one pence coins to 7 one pence coins to make 13 one pence coins.
(Note how the arrangement of the one pence coins makes this addition easier, 6 is set out as 5 + 1,   7 is set out as 5 + 2, the addition is 5 + 5 = 10 plus 1 + 2 = 3, making 13.)

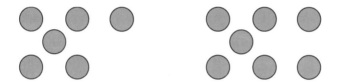

Now **TRADE** 10 one pence coins for 1 ten pence coin, leaving 3 one pence coins (units). The total for the one pence/units column is **3.** Put the traded ten pence coin in the tens column

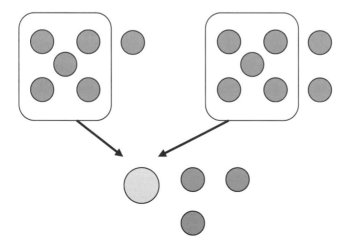

Now add the ten pence coins. Add 3 ten pence coins to 5 ten pence coins plus 1 ten pence (traded) coin to make 9 ten pence coins. The total for the ten pence/units column is **9**.

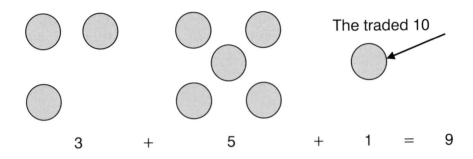

The traded 10

3   +   5   +   1   =   9

The answer is 93.   **36 + 57 = 93**

2. Using place value columns

Add together the numbers in the units (U) column. 6 + 7 = 13.
Thirteen is 3 units and 1 ten. Write **3** in the units column on the answer line and write **1** (actually 1 ten) at the top of the tens (T) column.

```
 T U
 1
 3 6
+5 7
   3
```

Add together the numbers in the tens (T) column. 3 + 5 + 1 = 9.
Write **9** in the tens column on the answer line.

```
 T U
 1
 3 6
+5 7
 9 3
```

The answer is 93.

68

3. Using numbers on their own.

This is the 'traditional' method. Tradition in the UK uses the word 'carrying' instead of 'trading'.

Start in the units column and add together the unit numbers:
$$6 + 7 = 13$$
Write the **3** units in the units column on the answer line.
Write the **1** (actually 1 ten) above the 3 at the top of the tens column

```
  1
  3 6
+ 5 7
    3
```

Add the numbers in the tens column: $3 + 5 + 1 = 9$.
Write **9** in the tens column on the number line.

```
  1
  3 6
+ 5 7
  9 3
```

The answer is 93.

Subtraction with trading in the units / tens columns

Example: 93 – 57 (This is the reverse of the addition example)

1. Using coins.

Start with the one pence coins. You need to subtract 7 coins, but you only have 3, so you must **trade**. Take one ten pence coin from the 9 in the tens column and trade it for 10 one pence coins. (This leaves 8 ten pence coins).

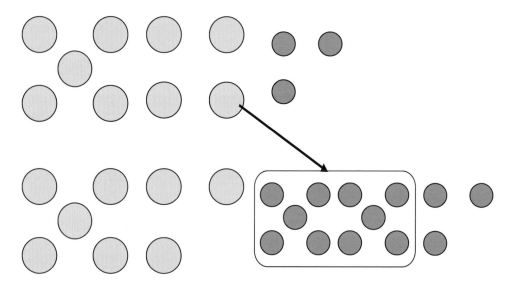

You now have 13 one pence coins and can subtract 7, 13 – 7 = 6. The answer in the one pence / units column is **6.**

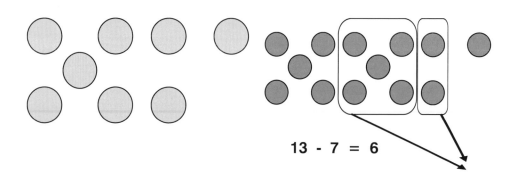

13 - 7 = 6

Now move to the ten pence coins.
There are 8 left and you must subtract 5:

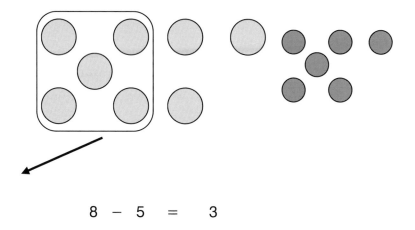

8 – 5 = 3

The answer in the ten pence / tens column is **3**.

The answer is 36.

2. Using place value columns

You have 3 in the upper position number in the units column. You need to subtract 7 from this 3 and since 3 is smaller than 7, you must **trade**.

```
  T│U
  9│3
- 5│7
   │
```

Take one ten from the 9 (tens) in the tens (T) column, leaving 8 and transfer this ten into the units (U) column to make 3 units up to 13.

It helps to introduce an extra row:

```
  T│U
  9│3
  8│13
- 5│7
   │6
```

The 93 is now written as: $80 + 13$

It is now possible to subtract 7 from 13:

$$13 - 7 = 6$$

Now move onto the tens (T) column.

You have to subtract 5 from 8: $\quad 8 - 5 = 3$

```
  T│U
  9│3
  8│13
- 5│7
  3│6
```

Write **3** on the answer line in the tens column. **The answer is 36.**

3. Using numbers on their own.

$$
\begin{array}{r}
\not{9}\ 3 \\
8\ {}^{1}3 \\
-\ 5\ 7 \\
\hline
3\ 6
\end{array}
\qquad
\begin{array}{r}
8 \\
\not{9}\ {}^{1}3 \\
-\ 5\ 7 \\
\hline
3\ 6
\end{array}
$$

This method does not always use a middle line, but can be set out as in the example on the right.

Practice exercise:

1a) 39 + 43   1b) 82 − 39

2a) 55 + 28   2b) 83 − 55

(Check your answers to these examples (page 149) before trying the rest. If you are wrong, re-read the section and work through the examples again.)

3) 28 + 34   4) 67 − 39

5) 75 + 17   6) 51 − 46

7) 34 + 56   8) 91 − 54

9) 86 − 47   10) 87 + 8

11) 72 − 53   12) 67 − 28

(answers on page 149)

Adding with trading in both the units / tens and tens / hundreds columns

Example: 67 + 74

1. Using coins (Reminder: £1 is 100p)

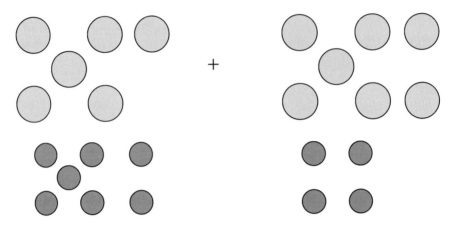

Start with the units. Add together the one pence coins. An overview of the clusters of 7 coins and 4 coins should show you that you can make two groups of 5 (making 10) with 1 left over, 7 + 4 = 11.

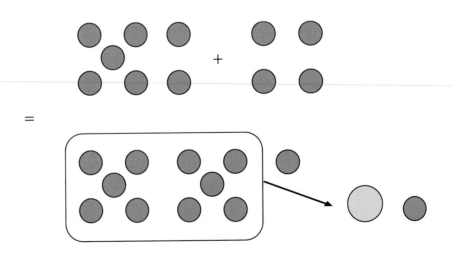

Now **trade** 10 x 1p coins for 1 x 10p coin, leaving one 1p coin (units). The total for the one pence / units place is **1**.

74

Transfer the traded ten pence coin in the ten pence / tens place.

Now add the 10p coins. An overview of the clusters of 6 coins and 7 coins shows you that you can make 10 x 10p coins (two groups of 5 x 10p coins). These are **traded** for a £1 coin (100). Left over, including the previously traded 10p coin, are 4 x 10p coins.
4 goes into the ten pence/tens place:

$$6 + 7 + 1 = 14$$

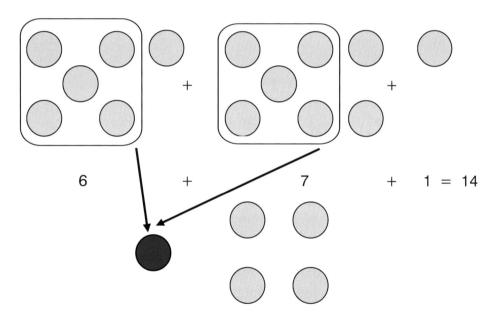

The traded £1 goes into the one pound / hundreds place.

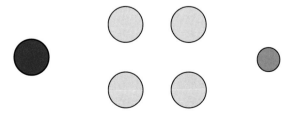

The answer is 141.

2. Using place value columns. $67 + 74$

```
  H | T | U
    | 6 | 7
+   | 7 | 4
```

Start with the units column.

Add together the numbers in the units (U) column: $7 + 4 = 11$

Eleven is 1 unit and 1 ten. Write the **1** unit in the answer space in the units column and write 1 (actually 1 ten) at the top of the tens (T) column.

```
  H | T | U
    | 1 |
    | 6 | 7
+   | 7 | 4
    |   | 1
```

Add together the numbers in the tens (T) column: $6 + 7 + 1 = 14$.
Write **4** on the answer line in the tens column.

```
  H | T | U
    | 1 |
    | 6 | 7
+   | 7 | 4
    | 4 | 1
```

Write the 1 from the 14 on the answer line in the hundreds column.

```
  H | T | U
    | 1 |
    | 6 | 7
+   | 7 | 4
  1 | 4 | 1
```

The answer is 141.

3. Using numbers on their own.

This is the 'traditional' method.

Start in the units column and add together the units numbers:

$$7 + 4 = 11$$

Write the **1** unit in the units column in the answer place.
Write 1 (actually 1 ten) above the 6 at the top of the tens column.

$$
\begin{array}{r}
\mathbf{1} \\
6\,7 \\
+\,7\,4 \\
\hline
\mathbf{1}
\end{array}
$$

Add the numbers in the tens column: $1 + 6 + 7 = 14$.
Write the **4** in the tens column in the answer place.

$$
\begin{array}{r}
\mathbf{1} \\
6\,7 \\
+\,7\,4 \\
\hline
\mathbf{4}\,1
\end{array}
$$

Write the **1** from the 14 on the answer line in the hundreds column.

$$
\begin{array}{r}
1 \\
6\,7 \\
+\,7\,4 \\
\hline
\mathbf{1}\,\mathbf{4}\,1
\end{array}
$$

The answer is 141.

Subtracting with trading in both the units / tens and tens / hundreds columns

Example: 141 - 74

An overview of the numbers tells us that trading will be needed to generate more units and more tens.

1. Using coins.

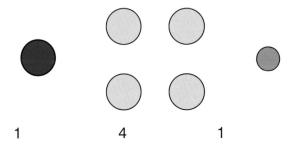

1   4   1

Start with the units. We need to subtract 4 units, but only 1 is available in 141. Trade one 10p coin for ten 1p coins:

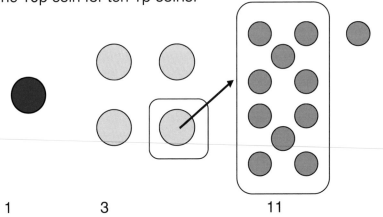

1   3   11

Now subtract 4 units.

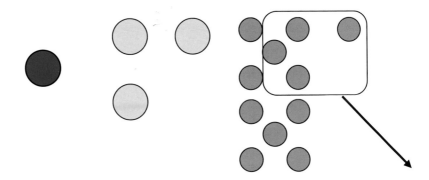

The intermediate answer is 137.

The next stage is to subtract 7 from the tens (10p). This requires trading the £1 coin for ten 10p coins:

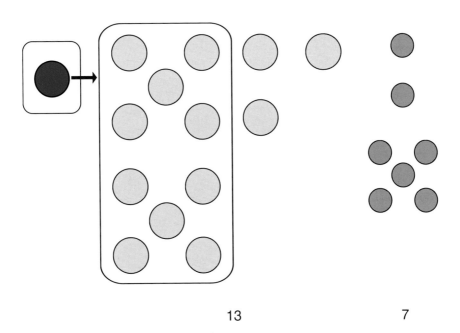

13   7

Stage 2 is to subtract seven 10p coins:

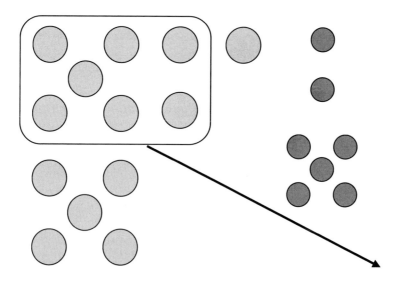

The final answer is 67.

2. Using place value columns.

```
H | T | U
1 | 4 | 1
—   7 | 4
```

Note that a line has been left for the trading (renaming/ decomposition).

Step 1. Trade one 10 for ten units:

```
H | T | U
1 | 4 | 1
  | 3 |11
- | 7 | 4
```

Then subtract 11 – 4

```
H | T | U
1 | 4 | 1
  | 3 |11
- | 7 | 4
  |   | 7
```

Step 2. Trade one 100 for ten tens:

```
H | T | U
1 | 4 | 1
  |13 |11      (Check by adding: 130 + 11 = 141)
- | 7 | 4
  |   | 7
```

Then subtract   13 – 7

```
H | T | U
1 | 4 | 1
  |13 |11
- | 7 | 4
  | 6 | 7
```

The final answer is 67.

3. Using numbers on their own.

This is the 'traditional' method.

```
    1 4 1
  -  7 4
```

Trade a ten for ten units:

```
      3  11
    1 4 1
  -   7 4
        7
```

Trade a 100 for ten tens:

```
    13 11
    1 4 1
  -   7 4
      6 7
```

The answer is 67.

Adding with trading in units / tens, tens / hundreds and hundreds / thousands

Example: 578 + 746

1. Using coins (and £10 note)
   (Reminder: £1 is 100p; £10 is 1000p)

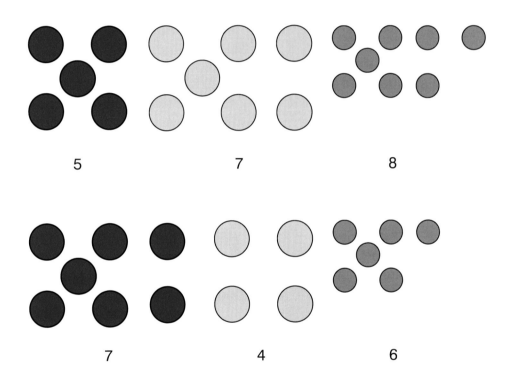

Start with the units (1p coins).
Add together the one pence coins / units. (Look at the patterns of the 8 and 6 and see a cluster of 5 in each of these numbers. The two 5 clusters add to make 10.)

$$8 + 6 = 14$$

14 is 4 units and 1 ten. The total in the units column is **4**.

H	T	U
	1	
5	7	8
+ 7	4	6
		4

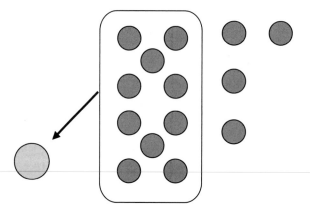

Trade 10 one pence coins for 1 ten pence coin and put the ten pence coin in the ten pence column.

Now add the tens.
Put together the ten pence coins: $1 + 7 + 4 = 12$
The **2** (20) goes as the total for the T/10p column.
The **1** (100) goes into the H/£1 column.

Th	H	T	U
	1	1	
	5	7	8
+	7	4	6
		2	4

Now add together the pound coins, again looking at the pattern of 5 clusters.

$1 + 5 + 7 = 13.$

From these 13 coins, **3** go as the total in the hundred/£1 column and 10 one pound coins are **traded** for **one** £10 note, which is placed in the thousands/£10 column.

Th	H	T	U
	1	1	
	5	7	8
+	7	4	6
1	3	2	4

The final answer is 1324.

2. Using place value columns.

Start with the units.

Add the two numbers in the units (U) column: $8 + 6 = 14$

Fourteen is 1 ten and 4 units. Write **4** in the answer place in the units column and write 1 for the ten at the top of the tens (T) column.

Th	H	T	U
		1	
	5	7	8
+	7	4	6
			4

Add the numbers in the tens column: $1 + 7 + 4 = 12$

The sum of this column is 12 tens. The 2 from the 12 is 2 tens. Write **2** in the answer place in the tens column. The 1 from the 12 is 10 tens, that is 1 hundred, so write **1** at the top of the hundreds (H) column.

Th	H	T	U
	1	1	
	5	7	8
+	7	4	6
		2	4

Finally, add the numbers in the hundreds (H) column:

$$1 + 5 + 7 = 13$$

The sum of this column is 13 hundreds.
The 3 from 13 is 3 hundreds, so write **3** in the answer place in the hundreds column.
The 1 from the 13 is ten hundreds, that is 1 thousand, so write **1** in the answer place in the thousands (Th) column.

Th	H	T	U
	1	1	
	5	7	8
+	7	4	6
1	3	2	4

The final answer is 1324.

3. Using numbers on their own.

As before, this is the 'traditional' method for addition.

Start in the units column and add together the unit numbers:
$$8 + 6 = 14$$
Write the **4** units on the answer line in the units column. Write the 1 (actually a ten) from 14 above the 7 at the top of the tens column.

```
  1
 578
+746
   4
```

Now add the numbers in the tens column including the 1 ten carried over from adding the unit numbers: $1 + 7 + 4 = 12$
Write the **2** from the 12 on the answer line of the tens column. Write the 1 from the 12 (actually 100) above the 5 in the hundreds column.

```
 11
 578
+746
  24
```

Now add the numbers in the hundreds column: $1 + 5 + 7 = 13$
Write the **3** from 13 on the answer line of the hundreds column and the **1** from 13 on the answer line for the thousands column.

$$
\begin{array}{r}
1\!1 \\
578 \\
+\ 746 \\
\hline
1324
\end{array}
$$

The final answer is 1324.

Subtracting with trading in units / tens, tens / hundreds and hundreds / thousands

Example: 1324 - 746

1. Using coins (and a £10 note):

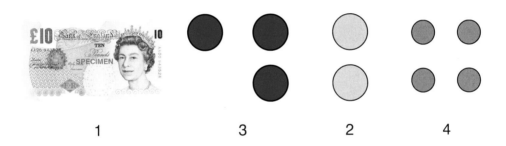

| 1 | 3 | 2 | 4 |

An overview of the numbers shows that trading (renaming/ decomposing) will be needed to generate more units, tens and hundreds.

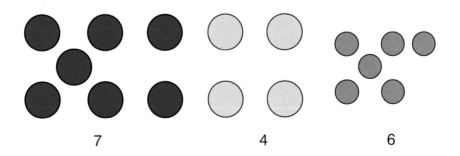

| 7 | 4 | 6 |

Start with units. There are 4 and we need to subtract 6, so a ten (10p) will have to be traded.

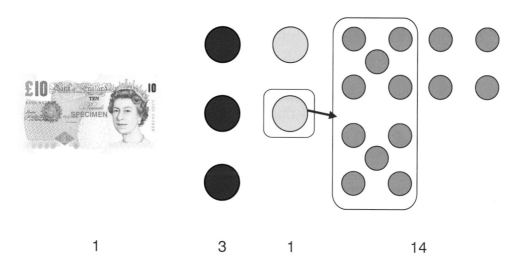

| 1 | | 3 | 1 | 14 |

Now subtract 6 units (1p coins):

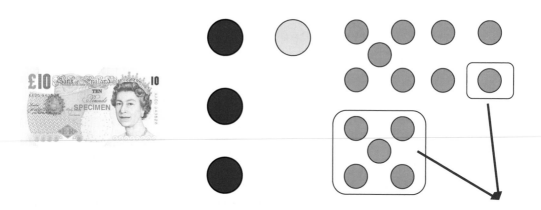

The intermediate answer is 131**8**

90

Now the tens. We need to subtract 4, so a £1 (100) will have to be traded for ten 10p coins

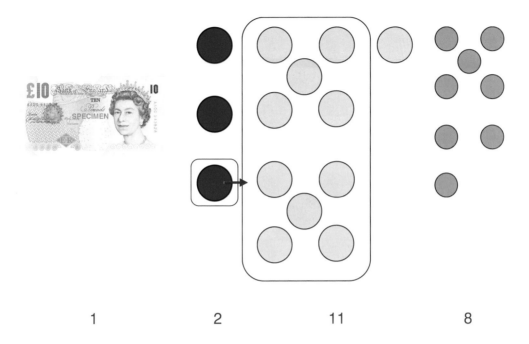

| 1 | 2 | 11 | 8 |

Now subtract four 10p coins:

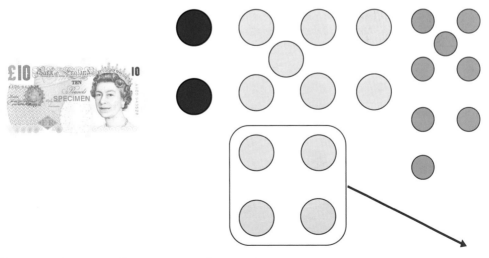

The new intermediate answer is **1278**.

Now the hundreds. We have to subtract 7, but there are only 2 one pound coins, so the £10 will be traded for 10 one pound coins.

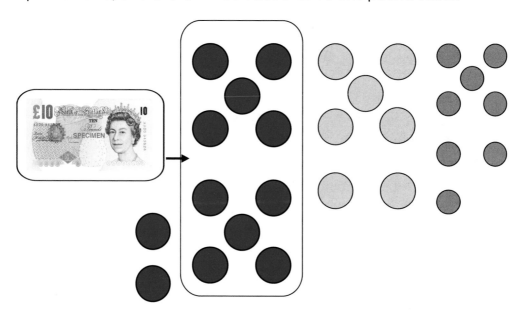

12   7   8

Now subtract 7 one pound coins (700)

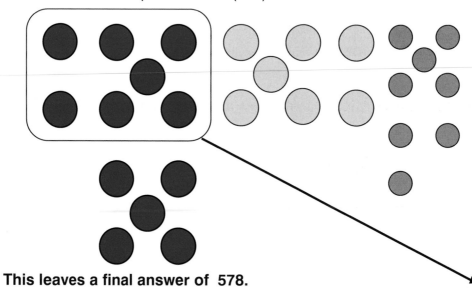

This leaves a final answer of 578.

2. Using place value columns.

Th	H	T	U
1	3	2	4
−	7	4	6

Note that an extra line is given for writing the traded numbers.

Overview the numbers: Trading will be needed to generate more units, tens and hundreds.

Step 1. Trade one 10 for ten units and subtract in the units column:

Th	H	T	U
1	3	2	4
		1	14
−	7	4	6
			8

Step 2. Trade one 100 for ten tens and subtract in the tens column:

Th	H	T	U
1	3	2	4
	2	11	14
−	7	4	6
		7	8

Step 3. Trade one 1000 for ten hundreds and subtract in the hundreds column:

Th	H	T	U
1	3	2	4
	12	11	14
−	7	4	6
	5	7	8

The final answer is 578.

3. Using numbers on their own. **1324 - 746**

```
  1 3 2 4
-   7 4 6
```

An overview of the numbers shows that trading is needed for units, tens and hundreds.

Start with units and trade from the tens. Subtract 6 from 14.

```
      1  14
  1 3 2 4
-   7 4 6
        8
```

Next trade from the hundreds. Subtract 4 from 11.

```
    2  11  14
  1 3 2 4
-   7 4 6
      7 8
```

Trade from the thousands. Subtract 7 from 12.

```
   12  11 14
  1 3 2 4
-   7 4 6
    5 7 8
```

The final answer is 578.

Practice exercise C

1a) 463 + 859   1b) 1322 − 859

2a) 682 + 939   2b) 1621 − 682

Check that your answers to 1a, 1b, 2a and 2b are correct, (page 149) before trying the other examples. If they are not correct, work through this section again, using coins and writing down the work.

For examples 3 to 12, look at the numbers in each question and make an estimate of the answer, as well as the "accurate" answer.

3)   777 + 444   4)   2821 − 654

5)   892 + 759   6)   6321 − 486

7)   348 + 878   8)   3427 − 1269

9)   987 + 965   10)   943 − 287

11)   1476 + 866   12)   6564 − 897

13)   1652 − 476   14)   1335 + 2898

(answers on page 149)

Adding involving a zero

Example: 467 + 234

1. Adding using coins.

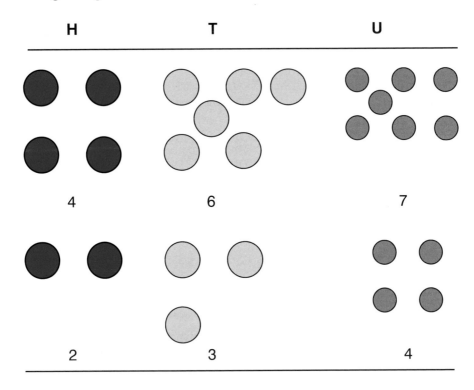

H	T	U
4	6	7
2	3	4

Start with the units:

Add together the one pence coins (units): $7 + 4 = 11$
The total is eleven, which is 1 ten and 1 unit.
Trade 10 one pence coins for 1 ten pence coin.
The **1** one pence coin is the answer in the units / 1p column.
The **1** ten pence coin should be placed in the tens / 10p column.

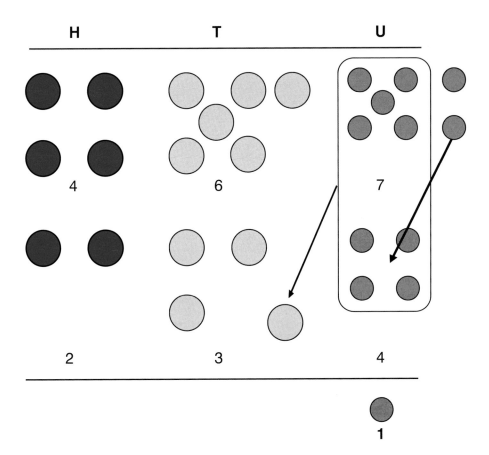

Now add together the ten pence coins, including the traded ten pence: 6 + 3 + 1 = 10.
Trade the 10 ten pence coins for 1 one pound coin.
Put the **1** one pound coin in the £1 / hundreds column.
The answer in the 10p / tens column is **0**.

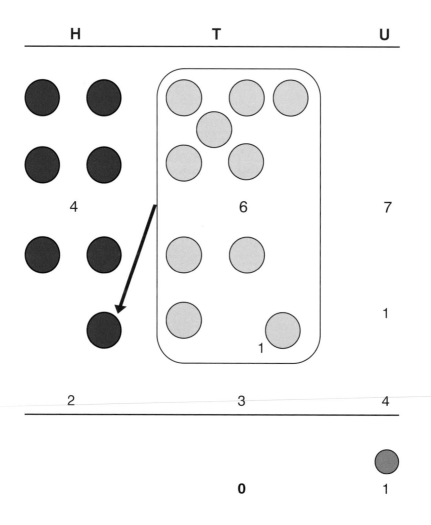

H   T   U

4   6   7

2   3   4

0   1

Now add the £1 coins: 4 + 2 + 1 = 7
The answer in the £1 / hundreds column is **7.**

H	T	U
4	6	7
2	3	4

H	T	U
7	0	1

The final answer is 701.

Subtracting with a zero

Example: 701 – 467

1. Subtracting demonstrated with coins.

This gives a clear explanation of trading (also called 'decomposition' or 'renaming') when there is a zero in the top number.

Start in the units column. You have to take 7 one pence coins away from 1 one pence coin, so you have to **trade** to generate more one pence coins. But there is a zero in the ten pence / tens column, which means that there are no ten pence coins to use for trading. Trading has to move to the next place value column, the £1 column, where there are coins available for trading.

There are two trading steps:

Step 1: Trade 1 one of the pound (100) coins for 10 of the 10p coins. Put them in the tens column.

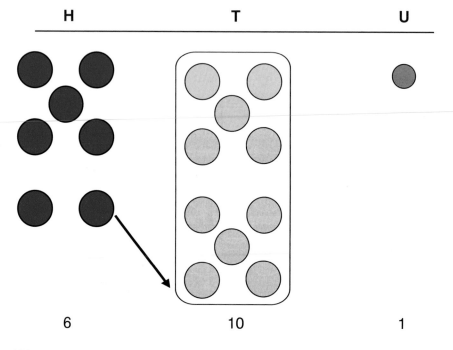

H	T	U
6	10	1

Step 2: Trade 1 of the ten pence coins for 10 one pence coins and put them in the 1p column.

H	T	U

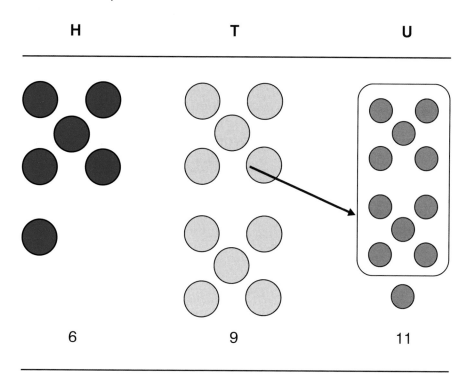

6	9	11

There are now 6 coins in the £1 column, 9 coins in the 10p column and 11 coins in the 1p column.

701 is now in the form:

$$
\begin{aligned}
6 \times 100 &= 600 \\
9 \times 10 &= 90 \\
11 \times 1 &= 11
\end{aligned}
$$

Adding these: $600 + 90 + 11 = 701$

The new arrangement has the same value. The 467 can now be subtracted as in previous examples and you will have **234** left.

2. Subtracting with place value columns.

Start in the units (U) column. You have to subtract 7, the units number in the lower line from 1, the units number in the upper line. This requires that you trade to get more units in the upper line.

But there is a zero in the tens column. There is no ten to trade.

So you have to move to the next place value column, the hundreds column.

It will help your layout of the work if you use an extra line for the trading/renaming/decomposition.

Step 1:

Trade 100 from the hundreds column to take into the tens column as 10 tens.

H	T	U
7	0	1
6	10	1
− 4	6	7

Step 2:

Trade 10 from the tens column to take 10 units into the units column.

H	T	U
7	0	1
6	9	11
− 4	6	7

The subtraction is now like our first example.

102

Start with the units: $11 - 7 = 4$
    Write **4** on the answer line in the units (U) column.

The tens (T) column: $9 - 6 = 3$
    Write **3** on the answer line in the tens (T) column.

The hundreds (H) column: $6 - 4 = 2$
    Write **2** on the answer line in the hundreds (H) column.

H	T	U
7	0	1
6	9	11
− 4	6	7
2	**3**	**4**

The answer is 234.

3. Using the numbers on their own.

Again, it may help to introduce an extra line for the trading/renaming/decomposition.

$$7\ 0\ 1$$

$$-\ 4\ 6\ 7$$

Start in the units column.
You need to trade to be able to subtract the 7 from the 1.
The tens column is zero so trading has to start in the hundreds column.
Trade 100 from the hundreds column into 10 tens for the tens column:

$$
\begin{array}{r}
7\ \ 0\ \ 1 \\
6\ 10\ 1 \\
-\ 4\ \ 6\ \ 7 \\
\end{array}
$$

What to do when you can't add and subtract

This provides numbers in the tens column for the next trade.

Trade 10 from the tens column into 10 units for the units column:

```
    7 0  1
    6 9 11
  – 4 6  7
```

The 701 is now ready for subtraction.

Check that the trading/renaming/decomposition is correct:

$$600 + 90 + 11 = 701$$

Start with the units: $11 - 7 = 4$.
Write **4** on the answer line in the units column.

The tens: $9 - 6 = 3$.
Write **3** on the answer line in the tens column.

The hundreds: $6 - 4 = 2$.
Write **2** on the answer line in the hundreds column.

```
    7 0  1
    6 9 11
  – 4 6  7
  ─────────
    2 3  4
```

The answer is 234.

104

Extra Stuff # 14

When a subtraction requires trading, then getting the right answer is helped by:

1) Layout/presentation:
   The extra line helps to keep the processes and numbers clear

2) Careful trading:
   You need to recognise when it is necessary to trade and then trade correctly, possibly thinking of the demonstrations with coins.

Practice exercise D

    1) 404 – 178   2) 606 – 88

(Check your answers to questions 1 and 2 now on page 149. If they are incorrect, work through this section again remembering to use the coins to help you understand each step).

    3) 704 – 546   4) 508 – 264

    5) 800 – 644   6) 200 – 67

    7) 602 – 586   8) 700 – 555

    9) 408 – 59   10) 901 – 768

(answers on page 149)

105

SUMMARY

You should now understand how to add and subtract, using trading where necessary. The same process applies to bigger numbers such as the thousands, ten thousands and all numbers.

Remember. **Overview before you start:** that is, look at all the numbers in the question before you start. Then:

    1) Make an estimate.

    2) Decide if you will need to trade to get the answer.

General practice exercise E

1) 46 + 32		2) 28 + 62	
3) 87 − 54		4) 72 − 29	
5) 103 − 47		6) 900 − 361	
7) 483 + 159		8) 943 − 258	
9) 1073 − 687		10) 4487 + 7846	

(answers on page 149)

MISTAKES THAT ARE OFTEN MADE

It sometimes helps to know what might go wrong so that you are aware of potential errors and can, hopefully, avoid them. The most common mistakes that people make when adding and subtracting are given below.

Mistakes people sometimes make when ADDING

1. Not putting the traded number into the proper place value column, for example:

$$
\begin{array}{r}
4\ 8\ 6 \\
+\ 2\ 6\ 7 \\
\hline
61413
\end{array}
$$

An estimate, for example, $500 + 250 = 750$ would show this answer is impossible.

2. Not lining up place values properly, for example:

$$
\begin{array}{r}
2\ 4\ 8\ 6 \\
+\ 6\ 4\ 1 \\
\hline
8\ 8\ 9\ 6
\end{array}
$$

Again, an estimate would show that this answer is impossible.

3. Making a zero mistake, for example:

$$
\begin{array}{r}
508 \\
+\ 261 \\
\hline
709
\end{array}
$$

The answer should be **769**.

4. Making a basic fact mistake, for example:

$$
\begin{array}{r}
648 \\
+ \ 237 \\
\hline
884
\end{array}
$$

$(8 + 7 = \mathbf{15}, \quad \text{NOT} \quad 14)$

The answer should be 885.

Extra Stuff # 15

This error is a 'dual tasking' error. The person is computing the question and trying to retrieve the basic fact 8 + 7. It is likely that the fact would be answered correctly in isolation, but work on the addition process 'blocks' the answer.

5. Not counting in the traded ten (or hundred etc), for example:

$$
\begin{array}{r}
764 \\
+ \ 178 \\
\hline
832
\end{array}
$$

The correct answer should be **94**2.

Estimating and errors

Making an estimate of an answer may help you to avoid errors, especially big errors.

One of the techniques that helps with estimating is rounding up and rounding down.

For example,   **589 + 823**

The 589 can be rounded to the nearest hundred: 600, rounding up

The 823 can also be rounded to the nearest hundred: 800, rounding down.

Now add the rounded numbers: 600 + 800 = 1400

1400 is the estimate.

Practice: Rounding up and rounding down.

Round these number to the nearest 100:

298	405	876
911	534	185
778	628	332

Mistakes people sometimes make when SUBTRACTING

Mistakes like these can be detected by estimation or by adding back the numbers to see if you arrive at the original number.

1. Always taking the smaller number from the bigger number, even when not appropriate. For example,

$$\begin{array}{r} 7\,6\,4 \\ -\,2\,5\,7 \\ \hline 5\,1\,3 \end{array}$$

This wrong answer was obtained by taking away 4 from 7 in the units column. Trading was needed from the tens column to give 14 units on the top line.

$$\begin{array}{r} 7\ 6\ \ 4 \\ 7\ 5\,14 \\ -2\ 5\ \ 7 \\ \hline 5\ 0\ \ 7 \end{array}$$

2. Taking away from zero. For example,

$$\begin{array}{r} 7\,0\,8 \\ -\,3\,4\,2 \\ \hline 4\,0\,6 \end{array}$$

The answer should be **36**6.

This wrong answer was obtained by taking away 4 from 0 and writing 0 as the answer. A hundred from the 7 should have been traded to give 10 tens in the tens column, as shown below.

$$\begin{array}{r} 7\ \ 0\ 8 \\ 6\,10\ 8 \\ -3\ \ 4\ 2 \\ \hline 3\ \ 6\ 6 \end{array}$$

3. Adding the two numbers instead of subtracting them. (Especially likely in exercises which mix addition and subtraction questions.)

4. Basic fact mistakes.
   For example,

$$\begin{array}{r} 9\ 8 \\ -\ 4\ 3 \\ \hline 5\ 6 \end{array}$$

The answer should be **55**.

5. Not lining up place values properly.
   For example,

$$\begin{array}{r} 9\ 5\ 6 \\ -\ 5\ 2\ \ \ \\ \hline 4\ 3\ 6 \end{array}$$

An estimate would show that this is an impossible answer.

The answer should be **904**:

$$\begin{array}{r} 9\ 5\ 6 \\ -\ 5\ 2 \\ \hline 9\ 0\ 4 \end{array}$$

6. Forgetting part of the trading process.
   For example,

$$\begin{array}{r} 4\ 3\ 1 \\ -2\ 6\ 0 \\ \hline 2\ 7\ 1 \end{array}$$

Trading created ten tens from one hundred, but the 4 hundred was not adjusted down to 3 hundred.

The answer should be **171**.

The correct procedure is:

$$
\begin{array}{r}
4\ \ \ 3\ \ 1 \\
3\ 13\ \ 1 \\
-\ 2\ \ \ 6\ \ 0 \\
\hline
1\ \ \ 7\ \ 1
\end{array}
$$

SUMMARY SO FAR

We have looked at:

Place value

For example:
In **2583, 2** is 2 thousands, **5** is 5 hundreds, **8** is 8 tens and **3** is 3 units.
In **3852, 3** is 3 thousands, **8** is 8 hundreds, **5** is 5 tens and **2** is 2 units.

The value an individual digit has depends on its relative place in the number. This is known as place value.

Trading

This relates to place value and is used in addition and subtraction sums.

For example, trading takes 1 hundred and trades it for 10 tens, or 1 ten and trades it for 10 units or, in reverse, trading takes 10 tens and trades them for 1 hundred, or 10 units and trades them for 1 ten.

For adding, this book concentrates on the word 'trading', largely because the demonstrations support the concept that is often attached to that word. In more traditional settings the word 'carried' is often used.

In subtraction this book again uses 'trading', since the process is the same in principle whether you are adding or subtracting.

In more traditional settings the words used are 'borrowing and paying back' or 'decomposing' or 'renaming'.

Basic facts

These are all the addition and subtraction facts for the numbers 0 to 10. They are all inter-related and one fact can be used to work out another. This helps memorising the facts and also shows how numbers can be used efficiently (and easily). Also remember to look for easy numbers within numbers (e.g. 7 is 5 + 2).

Written methods for addition and subtraction

The methods are the same, but reversed and can involve trading. You need to understand place value to be good at these sums.

Adding up columns of numbers

Adding up a lot of numbers, like a shopping bill, a restaurant bill or accounts can be difficult as this involves a series of additions. A mistake in any one of the component additions will make the final answer incorrect. The process can be made easier by using either of the two methods described below. You will have to try them to find which is the better one for you.

Method 1. 'Tens tallies.' (Hutchings's Low Stress Method)

Work through this example. Copy the numbers onto paper and follow each step. The principle is to use a tally for each time you reach 10, counting on in units only.

```
        8
    ₁ 7
    ₁ 9
    ₁ 7
  + 4
    3 5
```

Start at the top and add: 8 + 7 = 15

15 is 1 ten and 5 units. Put a tally by the 7 to represent the ten.

Add the 5 to 9, the next number down:

$$5 + 9 = 14$$

Write a tally for the ten and add the 4 to the next number down the column:

$$4 + 7 = 11$$

Another tally, next to the 7 and add the 1 unit to the next number down, 4:

$$1 + 4 = 5$$

5 is the unit digit for the answer. Count the tallies, 3, and this is the tens digit for the answer line.

The 'tally' method can be used for more complex additions. Sometimes the tallies are written as 'strike through' marks. For example:

```
    2    the total of the tallies from the units column
   4 6
   5 5
   2 3
 + 9 8
   2 2 2
```

Work through the next example:

```
    3
   8 7
   7 6
   6 9
 + 8 8
   3 2 0
```

Checking by estimating

Look at the 7 numbers in the example below. Of these 7 two digit
numbers, 3 were significantly above 50, 1 was close to 50 and 2 were
below 50.

$$
\begin{array}{r}
56 \\
32 \\
87 \\
67 \\
91 \\
25 \\
+\ 48 \\
\hline
406
\end{array}
$$

For two digit numbers, that is from 10 to 99, 50 is an easy number to
use as an approximate average value. (In this particular example the
average could be a little more than 50.)

As a rough check on the answer:

There are 7 two digit numbers with an average of about 50. Thus,
the total must be approximately 7 x 50 = 350.

Since we overviewed the numbers and gauged the average to be a
little more than 50, the answer should be more than 350.

Extra Stuff # 16

The technique above involves overviewing the numbers before starting the computation. This technique has been used before, for example, when looking at a subtraction to decide if trading is needed. Overviewing is a very important strategy in maths. It can help in very many ways.

Estimate first when trying this practice example.

$$
\begin{array}{r}
38 \\
41 \\
83 \\
76 \\
48 \\
27 \\
52 \\
85 \\
17 \\
+42 \\
\hline
\end{array}
$$

Estimate: There are 10 two digit numbers, fairly evenly distributed around 50:

Estimate at 10 x 50 = 500

Now compute the answer accurately with tallies:

Method 2. 'Taking out tens'

For this method you need to know the number bonds for 10 (4 + 6, etc). These need to be extended to combinations of three numbers (which add to make 10), for example, 5 + 4 + 1 and preferably some of the three number combinations which add to make 20, such as: 8 + 7 + 5 and 8 + 8 + 4.

$$0 \quad 1 \quad 2 \quad 3 \quad 4 \quad \mathbf{5} \quad 6 \quad 7 \quad 8 \quad 9 \quad 10$$
$$10 \quad 9 \quad 8 \quad 7 \quad 6 \quad \mathbf{5} \quad 4 \quad 3 \quad 2 \quad 1 \quad 0$$

The strategy is to scan down a column of digits and take out the pairs/combinations which make 10 and tally each 10 taken out.

For example:

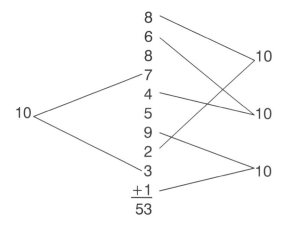

There are 4 pairs that make 10, giving 40.

Two numbers remain to be added: 8 + 5 = 13

The total is: 40 + 13 = 53

A two digit example:

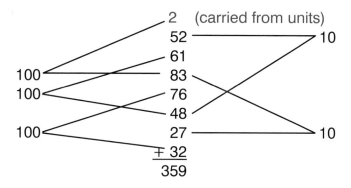

First the units: 7 + 3 and 8 + 2 make two ten number bonds, making 20. The three numbers left from the units column are 1 and 6 and 2.

$$1 + 6 + 2 = 9.$$

Write **9** on the answer line in the units column and write **2** (tens) at the top of the tens column.

Now look at the tens column:

There are 3 hundreds tallies and a digit 5 remains.
Write this **5** on the answer line in the tens column and write **3** for the three tallies on the answer line in the hundreds column.

The answer is 359.

Check against the estimate of 7 two digit numbers: 7 x 50 = 350

Extra Stuff # 17

Although we are looking for number bond to 10 combinations in the tens column, they actually add to 100.

For example, we combined 7 and 3 in the tens column in the example above. Because 7 is in the tens column it is actually 70 and similarly the 3 is 30, so the total is 100.

Now look another example, starting with the units column:

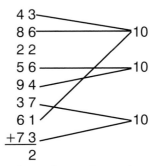

Leaving only the unpaired **2** to go into the units column.
Now look at the tens column:

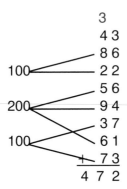

Add the unpaired numbers: 3 + 4 = 7 (really 30 + 40 = 70)
Add the tallied hundreds: 100 + 100 + 200 = 400

Check the answer, 472, against an **estimate:**
There are eight numbers, but 4 are significantly above 50 so using
50 x 8 = **400** will give a **low estimate.**

Practice exercise F

Choose the method you prefer and practise. If you are not sure which method you prefer, you might like to try both methods to see which is easier for you.

1)	42	2)	89
	61		15
	88		75
	37		23
	94		61
	23		23
	+ 75		+ 24

Check your answers to questions 1 and 2 (page 149). If you are correct carry on to the remaining questions. If you have made a mistake, check your working and/or work through the explanations again.

3)	71	4)	45
	69		56
	22		87
	44		50
	14		68
	+ 72		+ 25

5)	32	6)	19
	90		88
	62		72
	55		54
	68		47
	25		21
	+ 81		+ 36

7)   16   8)   67
        33   23
        92   49
        24   82
        27   84
        42   66
      +35   +49

9)   97   10)   55
        18   73
        61   68
        28   82
        46   28
        39   15
        21   21
        34   56
        89   32
      + 25   + 88

(answers are on page 149)

Make up some more examples for yourself. Try asking someone to give you some two digit numbers or take all the pence values of a supermarket bill (you will get a lot of 9s) and add them up or break up telephone numbers into two digits.

MENTAL ARITHMETIC Working 'in your head'

Doing sums in your head, mental arithmetic, requires several skills which often makes trying to use the same methods we for used for written procedures less effective.

Not least of these skills is memory, especially short term and working memories.

Consequently the methods described below are adaptations to make mental work easier. Because the procedures are different, you will need to practise and persevere, but learning these new strategies will have the additional benefit of helping you develop your understanding of numbers and arithmetic.

1. ADDING 9's

One of the best things about 9 is that it is 1 less than 10 and 10 is an easy number to add.

This strategy uses two easy steps instead of one hard step. The 'easy' steps are to add one ten and subtract one unit.

This strategy is an estimate followed by an adjustment of the estimate.

To add 9:

Step 1.   Add 10
Step 2.   Subtract 1

(Because adding 9 gives a smaller answer than adding 10.)

Extra Stuff # 18. Bigger or smaller?

Estimating is a very useful skill. Of course, there are no set rules as to how close an estimate should be to the accurate answer. Often that depends on the situation where the estimate is used.

Sometimes all that is needed of an estimate is, 'Is the answer going to be bigger or smaller?'

For example if we add 10 to a number instead of adding 9, is the answer bigger or smaller?

The answer is bigger. This tells us we have to subtract 1 to get the accurate answer.

For example:

$\qquad$ a) 76 + 9 is done in two steps:

Step 1. $\qquad$ 76 + 10 = 86
Step 2. $\qquad$ 86 − 1 = 85

$\qquad$ b) 64 + 9

Step 1. $\qquad$ 64 + 10 = 74
Step 2. $\qquad$ 74 − 1 = 73

The strategy can be extended to other numbers, for example:

To add 99:

1. $\qquad$ **Add 100**
2. $\qquad$ **Subtract 1**

For example:

$\qquad$ a) 874 + 99 is done in two steps:

Step 1. $874 + 100 = 974$
Step 2. $974 - 1 = 973$

    b) $697 + 99$

Step 1. $697 + 100 = 797$
Step 2. $797 - 1 = 796$

To add 95:

Step 1.   **Add 100**
Step 2.   **Subtract 5**

For example:
        a) $578 + 95$ is done in two steps:

Step 1. $578 + 100 = 678$
Step 2. $678 - 5 = 673$

    b) $1866 + 95$

Step 1. $1866 + 100 = 1966$
Step 2. $1966 - 5 = 1961$

To add 998:

Step 1.   **Add 1000**
Step 2.   **Subtract 2**

For example;
        a) $6579 + 998$ is done in two steps:

Step 1. $6579 + 1000 = 7579$
Step 2. $7579 - 2 = 7577$

b) 1297 + 998

Step 1.   1297 + 1000 = 2297
Step 2.   2297 –   2 = 2295

This procedure can be adapted to many numbers near to 10, 100, 1000 and so on.

It can also be used with money, especially those prices which are so popular in shops such as £9.99, £19.99 and so on.

For example, add together the following prices:

        £4.99   this is £ 5 less 1p
        £9.99   this is £10 less 1p
        £3.99   this is £ 4 less 1p
        £5.99   this is £ 6 less 1p

Step 1. Add the (rounded up) pounds:

            £5 + £10 + £4 + £6 = £25

Step 2. Subtract the 4 x 1p (= 4p):

            £25 minus 4p = **£24.96**

Books used to be priced as £5.95, £6.95, £14.95 and so on. The same strategy can be used for 95p prices. For example,

Add together the following prices:

        £4.95   which is £ 5 less 5p
        £5.95   which is £ 6 less 5p
        £3.95   which is £ 4 less 5p
        £9.95   which is £10 less 5p
        £4.95   which is £ 5 less 5p

Step 1. Add the (rounded up) pounds:

$$£5 + £6 + £4 + £10 + £5 = £30$$

Step 2. Subtract 5 x 5p (= 25p) from £30:

$$£30 \text{ minus } 25p = \textbf{£29.75}$$

Practice exercise G

Add together the prices:

1) £9.99 + £10.99 + £8.99 + £4.99 + £9.99

2) £4.99 + £4.99 + £4.99

Check the answers to these two questions (on page 149) before trying the rest. If you have made a mistake, check through your working and if you are still unsure read through the method again, trying out the examples with money.

3) £4.95 + £4.95 + £9.95 + £9.95

4) £19.95 + £14.95 + £24.95 + £29.95 + £9.95 + £4.95

5) £99.95 + £49.95

6) £1.99 + 99p + £2.99 + £1.99 + £4.99

(answers on page 149)

Subtracting 9's

The same idea is used, that is to use two easy steps instead of one hard step. The first easy step is subtracting 10 and the second easy step is adding 1.

Since 10 is bigger than 9, when you subtract 10 you get a smaller answer. The readjustment is made by **adding** back 1.

Try this with some coins, for example, **57 – 9**

Procedure 1:

Start with 57p set up as four 10p coins (40p) and seventeen 1p coins (17p).

Take away nine 1p coins to give an answer of **48.**

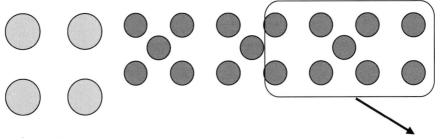

Procedure 2:

Start with 57p set up as five 10p coins and seven 1p coins.

Step 1. Take away one 10p coin

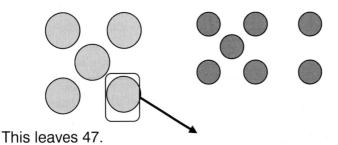

This leaves 47.

Step 2. Add one 1p coin.

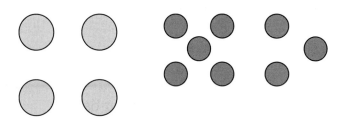

Giving an answer of **48.**

Try this with some other examples, using coins AND numbers each time.

To subtract 9:

Step 1.   Subtract 10
Step 2.   Add 1

Example: **57 − 9**

Step 1.   57 − 10 = 47
Step 2.   47 + 1 = **48**

To subtract 90:

Step 1.   Subtract 100
Step 2.   Add 10

Work this through with £1 and 10p coins. The process uses the fact
£1 − 10p = 90p

Example 1:   **684 − 90**

Step 1.   684 − 100 = 584

Step 2.   584 + 10 = **594**

Example 2:   **5879 – 90**

Step 1. $5879 - 100 = 5779$
Step 2. $5779 + 10 = \mathbf{5789}$

To subtract 95:

Step 1.   Subtract 100
Step 2.   Add 5

Example: **673 – 95**

Step 1. $673 - 100 = 573$
Step 2. $573 + 5 = \mathbf{578}$

To subtract 990:

Step 1.   Subtract 1000
Step 2.   Add 10

Example: **7864 – 990**

Step 1. $7864 - 1000 = 6864$
Step 2. $6864 + 10 = \mathbf{6874}$

To subtract 8:

Step 1. Subtract 10
Step 2. Add 2

Example: **64 – 8**

Step 1. $64 - 10 = 54$
Step 2. $54 + 2 = 56$

This procedure can be adapted to many numbers near to 10, 100, 1000 etc.

2. GENERAL ADDITION

The demands of mental arithmetic on memory can sometimes be reduced by using methods which offer more support. For example, one of the ways people use to help remember something is to repeat it (sometimes out loud) several times.

We read numbers from left to right. For example, 645 is said as 'six hundred and forty five'.

However, in written arithmetic we add from right to left (units, tens, hundreds, etc).

In mental addition if you do the opposite and add from left to right, you start with what is effectively an estimate and repeat the early numbers as you work through the example, thus supporting short term memory.

Always overview the question before you start. Look at the values of the numbers, see if there is any trading, form a broad estimate.

Adding left to right, with no trading

Example: **134 + 632**

Overview and estimate:
The numbers will not result in any trading.
An estimate by adding the hundreds only: 100 + 600 = 700.
Including the tens brings the estimate closer to, but still less than, 800.

Hundreds. Start with the hundreds: add 1 hundred to 6 hundred:
        1 + 6 = 7. So we have seven hundred and…

Tens. Add the tens: 3 tens add 3 tens, 3 + 3 = 6.
        So we have seven hundred and sixty...

Units. Add the units: 4 + 2 = 6.
        So the answer is seven hundred and sixty six.
                134 + 632 = 766

As we worked through this problem, we repeated seven hundred three times and seven hundred and sixty twice. We also constructed the answer in the same order as its final form (with right to left addition, the digits are constructed in reverse).

Adding left to right, with trading

Example: **462 + 379**

Overview and estimate:
There will be trading in the units and hundreds columns.
An estimate using only hundreds is 400 + 300 = 700.
Adding in the tens takes the estimate to over 800.

Hundreds. Start with the hundreds: add $4 + 3 = 7$,

   The answer so far is **seven hundred...**

Tens. Add the tens digits: $6 + 7 = 13$ tens.

13 tens are 130 which is 1 hundred and 30, so the 1 hundred should be added to the existing 7 hundred: $7 + 1 = 8$ hundred.

   The answer so far is **eight hundred and thirty ...**

Units. Add the units digits: $2 + 9 = 11$ units

11 units are 1 ten and 1 unit, so the 1 ten should be added to the existing thirty to make forty.

The final answer is 841.

Practice exercise H

Try adding these examples in your head.

1) 45 + 43   2) 67 + 32

3) 36 + 47   4) 78 + 15

5) 453 + 346   6) 134 + 762

7) 673 + 264   8) 332 + 291

9) 775 + 366   10) 609 + 494

3. GENERAL SUBTRACTION

The written method we used for subtraction is quite demanding if used as a mental arithmetic method. It requires an ability to visualise and hold that image in memory for a time which is compounded by the several steps involved in the method. Subtraction when done as mental arithmetic is often harder to do than addition.

There are some 'special cases', but first, as with addition, look at a method which works (or subtracts) by moving through the numbers from left to right.

Subtracting from left to right

As with addition it is advisable to overview to see if the problem is one which will require trading and make an estimate of the answer.

Example 1:   **487 – 163**

Overview and estimate:
The numbers do not require any trading.
An estimate focusing only on the hundreds is   400 – 100 = 300.
If the tens are also considered then they make the answer a little above 300.

Hundreds. Subtract the hundreds: 4 – 1 = 3 hundreds.

The answer so far is three hundred and …

Tens. Subtract the tens: 8 – 6 = 2 tens.

The answer so far is three hundred and twenty ..

Units. Subtract the units: 7 – 3 = 4 units.

The final answer is three hundred and twenty four: 324

Example 2.   **632 – 186**

Overview and estimate:
Trading will be needed for units and tens.
An estimate focusing on hundreds is 600 – 100 = 500.
If the tens are also considered then the estimate of 500 has to be lowered, possibly to 450.

Hundreds. Subtract the hundreds: 6 – 1 = five hundreds.

The answer so far is five hundred and …

Tens. Subtract the tens: 3 – 8. This requires trading:
Reduce the hundreds to four hundred and move the hundred
(= 10 tens) to the tens column.
$$13 - 8 = 5$$

The answer so far is four hundred and fifty ….

Units. Subtract the units: 2 – 6 . This requires trading:
Reduce the tens to forty and move the ten (= 10 units) to the units column.
$$12 - 6 = 6.$$

The final answer is four hundred and forty six: 446

Any new skill requires practise. Arithmetic skills are no exception. These new procedures may feel strange at first. Try to persevere and give the ideas time to work.

However, no one method works for everyone. The only way to find out if it works for you is to work on understanding how the method works and then give it a fair try.

Counting on

This strategy works particularly well with subtractions from 100s, 1000s, 10,000s, etc. Number bonds for 10 are especially useful in these cases.

The principle is to start with the units, adding on the number needed to make 10.

Then move to the tens and add on the number to make 100.

Then move to the hundreds and add on the number to make 1000.

(These processes are sometimes called 'crossing the tens/ hundreds/'etc.)

Start with the units digit from the subtracting number. When you first work through these examples, use coins (and trading) to show the procedure.

Example 1:   **6000 - 2349**

Overview and estimate:
Counting on will cross the tens, hundreds and thousands.
An estimate using only thousands is 6000 – 2000 = 4000.
If the hundreds are also considered then the estimate will be closer to 3500.

Start with the 9 (from 234**9**)

Units. Add **1** to 9 to make 10:   2349 becomes 2350

Tens. Add **5** to 5 (from 23**5**0) to make 10:   2350 becomes 2400

Hundreds. Add **6** to 4 (from 2**4**00) to make 10:   2400 becomes 3000

Thousands. Add **3** to 3 (from **3**000) to make 6:   3000 becomes 6000

You have counted on **3** thousands, **6** hundreds, **5** tens and **1** unit.

The answer is 3651.

Check by adding:
$$\begin{array}{r} 2349 \\ + \ 3651 \\ \hline 6000 \end{array}$$

Example 2:   **800 – 312**

Overview and estimate:
Counting on will cross the tens and hundreds.
An estimate using only the hundreds is 800 – 300 = 500. Considering the tens only reduces this estimate to slightly below 500.

Units.   312 +   **8**   = 320

Tens.   320 + **80** = 400

Hundreds.   **400 + 400**   = 800

The answer is 488

Check by adding:
$$\begin{array}{r} 312 \\ + 488 \\ \hline 800 \end{array}$$

Now try an example with money: **£20 - £13.26**

Overview and estimate:
There will be a need to cross trade the ten pence and pound.
An estimate just using the pounds is £20 - £13 = £7.
If the pence are also considered then the estimate is reduced to something bigger than £6.50.

One pence.   £13.2**6** +   **4p** = £13.30

Ten pence.   £13.**30** +   **70p** = £14.00

One pound.   £14.00 + **£6**.00 = £20.00

The answer is **£6.74**

Check by adding: £13.26
                                 + £ 6.74
                                   £20.00

Practice exercise I

   1)   500 – 327   2)   700 – 482

Check your answers to these two questions on page 149. If they are
correct carry on with questions 3 to 12. If they are not correct, work
through the examples again, remembering to use the coins in your
first run through.

   3)   1000 – 609   4)   800 – 333

   5)   £10.00 - £3.95   6)   £20.00 - £16.45

   7)   £100.00 - £67.36   8)   2000 – 1812

   9)   300 – 87   10)   £5.00 - £2.12

   11)   £5000 - £1756.50   12)   4000 – 2614

(answers on page 149)

Equal additions with tens

This is also a written method. It is easy to explain if you use algebra, but not as easy to explain with coins. It is an alternative to trading. It is another way of generating more units.

The basic idea is to add ten to the units column of the top number and balance this by adding ten to the tens column of the bottom number.

For example, **64 – 38**

Step 1. Add ten units to the top number:

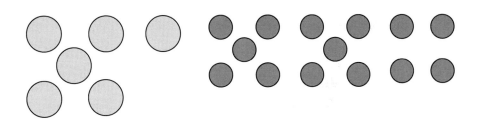

64 becomes 74 (as 60 + 14)

Step 2. Add ten to the bottom number in the tens column:

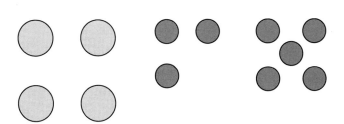

38 becomes 48

Step 3. Subtract:

$$\begin{array}{cc} \mathbf{T} & \mathbf{U} \\ 6 & 4 \\ -\ 3 & 8 \\ \hline \end{array} \qquad \begin{array}{cc} \mathbf{T} & \mathbf{U} \\ 6 & 14 \\ -\ 4 & 8 \\ \hline 2 & 6 \end{array}$$

Check by adding:
$$\begin{array}{r} 26 \\ +\ 38 \\ \hline 64 \end{array}$$

This method works for all place values.

For example,   **438 – 173**

Step 1. Subtract in the units column: $8 - 3 = 5$
Step 2. Add ten tens (100) to the top digit in the tens column, making 3 tens into 13 tens.

Subtract $13 - 7 = \mathbf{6}$

$$\begin{array}{ccc} \mathbf{H} & \mathbf{T} & \mathbf{U} \\ 4 & 3 & 8 \\ -\ 1 & 7 & 3 \\ \hline \end{array} \qquad \begin{array}{ccc} \mathbf{H} & \mathbf{T} & \mathbf{U} \\ 4 & 13 & 8 \\ -\ 2 & 7 & 3 \\ \hline 2 & 6 & 5 \end{array}$$

Step 3. Add the (equal) one hundred to the 1 (hundred) on the bottom line to make 2 hundred.
          Subtract in the hundreds column: $4 - 2 = \mathbf{2}$

The answer is **265.**

Check by addition:
$$\begin{array}{r} 265 \\ +173 \\ \hline 438 \end{array}$$

Equal additions can be used in more than one column.

For example,   **614 – 378**

Overview and estimate:
If the trading method was being used, then trading would be needed from tens and hundreds.
In this procedure, equal additions are needed for units/tens and for tens/hundreds.
An estimate would be better and easier if 378 was rounded up to 400, giving 600 – 400 = 200. This will be an under-estimate.

Step 1.   Equal additions for the units:

H	T	U
6	1	4
– 3	7	8

H	T	U
6	11	14
– 3	**8**	8
2	3	6

Step 2. Equal additions for the tens:

H	T	U
6	1	4
– 3	7	8

H	T	U
6	**11**	14
– **4**	8	8
2	3	6

Step 3. Subtract.

Check by addition: 236
                          + 378
                             614

Balance and adjust

This is a similar strategy to rounding up 9 to 10. The idea is to adjust one of the numbers to make the subtraction procedure easier and then adjust back. You make it two easy steps, rather than one hard step by changing one of the numbers in the problem.

Example: **86 – 38**

Overview and estimate:
8 is bigger than 6 (by 2), so trading would be needed if we use the 'traditional' method.
In this method we adjust by adding 2 to the 86 so that the initial subtraction in the units column gives zero.

An estimate would be to subtract the tens: 80 – 30 = 50

Step 1.
$$\begin{array}{r} 86 \\ -\ 38 \\ \hline \end{array}$$

Make the units column subtraction easier by 'balancing'.
The adjustment should make the answer in the units column 0.
So here you add 2 to the top number.

$$\begin{array}{r} 88 \\ -\ 38 \\ \hline \end{array}$$

Step 2. Subtract:

$$\begin{array}{r} 88 \\ -\ 38 \\ \hline 50 \end{array}$$

Step 3. This intermediate answer (an estimate) is too big since the top number was made bigger. To adjust back to a precise answer, subtract the 2 you added in Step 1:

$$50 - 2 = 48$$

The answer is **48.**

Check by adding:

$$
\begin{array}{r}
48 \\
+ \ \underline{38} \\
86
\end{array}
$$

Practice exercise J

    1) 73 – 27   2) 94 – 68   3) 51 – 36

    4) 67 – 38   5) 81 – 34   6) 42 - 17

Addition/subtraction facts square

+	0	1	2	3	4	5	6	7	8	9	10
0	0	1	2	3	4	5	6	7	8	9	10
1	1	2	3	4	5	6	7	8	9	10	11
2	2	3	4	5	6	7	8	9	10	11	12
3	3	4	5	6	7	8	9	10	11	12	13
4	4	5	6	7	8	9	10	11	12	13	14
5	5	6	7	8	9	10	11	12	13	14	15
6	6	7	8	9	10	11	12	13	14	15	16
7	7	8	9	10	11	12	13	14	15	16	17
8	8	9	10	11	12	13	14	15	16	17	18
9	9	10	11	12	13	14	15	16	17	18	19
10	10	11	12	13	14	15	16	17	18	19	20

Addition/subtraction facts square

+	0	1	2	3	4	5	6	7	8	9	10
0	0	1	2	3	4	5	6	7	8	9	10
1	1	2	3	4	5	6	7	8	9	10	11
2	2	3	4	5	6	7	8	9	10	11	12
3	3	4	5	6	7	8	9	10	11	12	13
4	4	5	6	7	8	9	10	11	12	13	14
5	5	6	7	8	9	10	11	12	13	14	15
6	6	7	8	9	10	11	12	13	14	15	16
7	7	8	9	10	11	12	13	14	15	16	17
8	8	9	10	11	12	13	14	15	16	17	18
9	9	10	11	12	13	14	15	16	17	18	19
10	10	11	12	13	14	15	16	17	18	19	20

Blank squares

+	0	1	2	3	4	5	6	7	8	9	10
0											
1											
2											
3											
4											
5											
6											
7											
8											
9											
10											

+	0	1	2	3	4	5	6	7	8	9	10
0											
1											
2											
3											
4											
5											
6											
7											
8											
9											
10											

Extra Stuff # 19

When you practise filling in the facts on the addition and subtraction square you do not have to fill them in in number order. Start by filling in the number facts you know best or the key facts (it would be good if these were the same facts).

Answers to Exercises

p 66 1a) 76   1b) 31   2a) 97   2b) 75
        3a) 88   3b) 54   4a) 64   4b) 41   5) 83
        6) 30   7) 65   8) 31   9) 31   10) 46

p 73 1a) 82   1b) 43   2a) 83   2b) 28
        3) 62   4) 28   5) 92   6) 5   7) 90
        8) 37   9) 39   10) 95   11) 19   12) 39

p 95 1a) 1322   1b) 463   2a) 1621   2b) 939
        3) 1221   4) 2167   5) 1651   6) 5835
        7) 1226   8) 2158   9) 1952   10) 656
        11) 2342   12) 5667   13) 1176   14) 4233

p 105 1) 226   2) 518   3) 158   4) 244   5) 156
        6) 133   7) 16   8) 145   9) 349   10) 133

p 106 1) 78   2) 90   3) 33   4) 43   5) 56
        6) 539   7) 642   8) 685   9) 386   10) 12333

p 121 1) 420   2) 310   3) 292   4) 331   5) 413
        6) 337   7) 269   8) 420   9) 458   10) 518

p 127 1) £44.95   2) £14.97   3) £29.80
        4) £104.70   5) £149.90   6) £12.95

P.133 1) 88   2) 99   3) 83   4) 93   5) 799
        6) 896   7) 937   8) 623   9) 1141   10) 1103

p 138 1) 173   2) 218   3) 391   4) 467
        5) £6.05   6) £3.55   7) £32.64   8) 188
        9) 213   10) £2.88   11) £3243.50   12) 1386

p.143 1) 46   2) 26   3) 15
        4) 29   5) 47   6) 25